EDMONIA

Wildfire in Marble

LEWIS

A PEOPLE IN FOCUS BOOK

EDMONIA
Wildfire in Marble
LEWIS

Rinna Evelyn Wolfe

DILLON PRESS
PARSIPPANY, NEW JERSEY

Acknowledgments

I wish to thank Barbara Fields, Adelene Foster, Marjorie Jackson, and my editor, Debbie Biber, for patiently reading this manuscript, and also librarians Joan Goddard and Bob Johnson, of the Martin Luther King, Jr., San Jose Public Library (California Room). Their ideas and materials added enriching details to the story of Edmonia Lewis's life.

I am especially indebted to Timothy Burgard, American Art Curator of the De Young Museum, San Francisco, California, and to George Gurney, Curator of Sculpture, National Museum of American Art, Smithsonian Institution. Their gifts of time, their wisdom, and the unpublished information they shared enhanced Edmonia Lewis's story greatly.

Photo Credits
Front cover: Boston Athenaeum. Back cover: Art Resource, NY/National Museum of American Art, Washington, DC/Gift of Joseph S. Sinclair.

Art Resource, NY/National Museum of American Art, Washington, DC: 60, 70, 91, 98; Gift of Joseph S. Sinclair: 77; Gift of Alfred T. Morris, Sr.: 89; Gift of Warren Robbins: 90; National Portrait Gallery, Washington, DC: 10, 55. Boston Athenaeum: 57. The Granger Collection, New York: 9. Courtesy, the Harvard University Portrait Collection, Harvard University Art Museum: 81. Howard University Gallery of Art: 61, 75 *l.*, *r.* The Metropolitan Museum of Art, gift of John Taylor Johnston, 1888: 94 *r.* The Museum of Afro American History: 48. National Archives: 13. Oberlin College Archives, Oberlin, OH: 22, 25, 26, 27, 35. San Jose Public Library, California Room: 7 *t.*, *b.*, 8, 86, 87. Schlesinger Library, Radcliffe College: 117. Schomberg Center for Research in Black Culture: 2. © 1995 Sotheby's, Inc./Courtesy, the Walter O. Evans Collection: 74. Gift of the Class of 1886/Photograph © Davis Museum and Cultural Center, Wellesley College, Wellesley, MA: 94 *l.*

Library of Congress Cataloging-in-Publication Data
Wolfe, Rinna.
    Edmonia Lewis: wildfire in marble/by Rinna Evelyn Wolfe.—1st ed.
        p.   cm.—(A people in focus book)
    Includes bibliographical references and index.
    ISBN 0-382-39713-4 (lib. bdg.).—ISBN 0-382-39714-2 (pbk.)
    1. Lewis, Edmonia—Juvenile literature. 2. Ogibwa Indians—
Biography—Juvenile literature. 3. Afro-American sculptors—
Biography—Juvenile literature. I. Title. II. Series.
NB237.L487W66 1998
730'.92—dc21
  [B]   97-14807

Summary: A biography of an inventive sculptor with dual racial heritage—Chippewa and African American—who overcame prejudice and poverty to give to the world a visual tribute to her people.

Cover design by Michelle Farinella
Book design by Lisa Ann Arcuri

Published by Dillon Press
A Division of Simon & Schuster
299 Jefferson Road, Parsippany NJ 07054
First Edition
Printed in the United States of America
10 9 8 7 6 5 4 3 2 1

Contents

INTRODUCTION

There they were—treasures almost 100 years old. Cautiously historian Philip Montesano stepped toward a dusty, cobweb-covered clump in the basement of the city library of San Jose, California. The year was 1967.

Bending down, he focused his flashlight on three sculptures. Just hours earlier he had read about what he might find. He peered at the first figure. There was no mistake. He was looking into the "sunken eyes, the familiar outline of hair and beard—Abraham Lincoln."[1]

Later, describing his discovery, he wrote, "I tore at . . . the grime until pure marble glowed."[2] Then Montesano rubbed the other statues until inscriptions became visible. He read the words etched into the bases of two sculptures of cuddling, angelic children:

Edmonia Lewis, ASLEEP, 1871, Roma

Edmonia Lewis, AWAKE, 1872, Roma

Today Edmonia Lewis's three statues rest on individual pedestals on the library's main level.

Asleep

Awake

Abraham Lincoln

Visitors who pause to admire the silken polished marble children and the serious Lincoln must wonder, "Why are these figures here?" and "Who was Edmonia Lewis?"

Edmonia Lewis's story begins in the mid-1800s, when the United States was on the brink of turbulent times. The twenty-eight southern and northern states, edging toward civil war, were quarreling over slavery. This hotly debated issue threatened to split the country apart.

On New Year's Day, 1831, more than a decade before Edmonia was born, 24-year-old William Lloyd Garrison published his historic antislavery newspaper, *The Liberator.* "I have a system to destroy and no time to waste,"[3] he said. And in his newspaper he wrote the following:

. . . My name is "Liberator"!
To hurl my shafts at freedom's deadliest foes
My task is hard—for I am charged to save
Man from his brother—to redeem the slave![4]

Across the country, groups were organizing against slavery. Either two or three years after Edmonia's birth, Frederick Douglass published his autobiography, *Narrative of the Life of Frederick Douglass, An American Slave.* This exceptional book alerted thousands to the horrors of a slave's life. Then, in 1852, Harriet Beecher Stowe's novel *Uncle Tom's Cabin* also revealed the evils of slavery. Nevertheless, many citizens in the North and South considered black people personal property. Unrest was widespread.

William Lloyd Garrison

No one could foretell that Edmonia would one day meet both Douglass and Garrison or that these men would become kind, supportive friends.

Frederick Douglass

Edmonia lived in a time when women had few choices. Society expected them to become servants or teachers or to marry and raise families. Edmonia chose instead to be a sculptor, and this decision eventually led her to Rome, Italy, far from her native country.

Edmonia was proud of her dual cultural heritage—Chippewa and African American. An inventive, highly energetic child, she grew into a vibrant, strong-willed independent woman.

While Garrison, Douglass, Stowe, and others crafted words that helped to end slavery, Edmonia's statues honored pioneering men and women who had struggled to gain justice, liberty, and equality for all people.

Edmonia was a self-reliant woman and a woman of "color." Because she dared to be a sculptor when few women, black or white, became artists, she had to struggle to overcome prejudice and, at times, severe poverty. Even though her works commanded good prices into the late 1870s, Edmonia realized early on that she was a loner and an outsider.

Periods of Edmonia Lewis's life still remain clouded in mystery. Yet the figures she carved reveal her courage, ideals, and integrity.

Today those who have an opportunity to see and admire her works may be amazed at the history in sculpture that Edmonia Lewis has given to the world. Too few people, however, realize that a Chippewa–African American woman carved these gleaming white marble figures more than 100 years ago.

Forgotten for over a century, Edmonia Lewis finally is being rediscovered.

Chapter
1

Edmonia's Chippewa Heritage

*L*ittle is known about Mary Edmonia Lewis's earliest years, and historians disagree about the date of her birth. Some researchers believe she was born July 14, either 1844 or 1845, in the tiny village of Greenbush, near Albany, New York. Edmonia's passport, signed in 1865, lists her birthdate as July 4, 1844. Yet we know that after the Civil War many freed slaves chose July 4th, America's Independence Day, as their birthday. Edmonia's birth date is still uncertain, but the year 1844 appears to be accurate.

Edmonia's father, a free African from the West Indies, probably came from Haiti. Her mother was Chippewa, or Ojibwa. The word *Chippewa* means "people who make pictographs." She was a member of the Mississauga band who lived near Lake Ontario in

Edmonia Lewis's passport lists her birthdate as July 4, 1844.

Residence, *Boston*

Age, *20*

Stature, *4 feet*

Forehead, *high*

Eyes, *Black*

Nose, *Small*

Mouth, *Medium*

Chin, *Small*

Hair, *Black*

Complexion, *Black*

Face, *Oval*

Passport —
To be sent
to George F. Baker
New York

I, *M. Edmonia Lewis* of *Boston* in the State of *Mass* do solemnly swear that I am a *Native* and Loyal Citizen of the United States of America, and about to travel abroad, That I was born in *Greenbush New York* on or about the *4th* day of *July* *1844*

M. Edmonia Lewis

I, *M. P. Kennard* of *Boston* in the State of *Mass:* do solemnly Swear that *M. Edmonia Lewis* now present, is personally known to me, and that to the best of my knowledge and belief the foregoing Declaration, made and signed by him in my presence, is true.

M. P. Kennard

Commonwealth of Massachusetts.

SUFFOLK, SS. }
BOSTON.

On this *Twenty first* day of *August* A. D. Eighteen Hundred and *Sixty five* personally appeared before me, JONATHAN AMORY, a Notary Public for the County of Suffolk, duly appointed and sworn, *M. P. Kennard* and *M. Edmonia Lewis* and severally solemnly Swore to the truth of the foregoing Declarations, by them subscribed, according to the best of their knowledge and belief.

In Testimony Whereof, I have hereunto set my hand, and affixed my Seal of Office, the day and year above written.

Jonathan Amory
Notary Public

I, *M. Edmonia Lewis* do solemnly Swear that I will support, protect, and defend the Constitution and Government of the United States against all enemies, whether domestic or foreign; and that I will bear true faith, allegiance, and loyalty to the same, any ordinance, resolution, or law of any State convention or legislature to the contrary notwithstanding; and, further, that I do this with a full determination, pledge, and purpose, without any mental reservation or evasion whatsoever; and, further, that I will well and faithfully perform all the duties which may be required of me by law: So help me God.

M. Edmonia Lewis

Sworn to and subscribed before me, this *Twenty first* day of *August* A. D. one thousand eight hundred and sixty *five*

Jonathan Amory
Justice of the Peace
Not. Pub.

Canada. Edmonia's much older brother, Samuel, was born in Haiti, and his Chippewa name was Sunrise.

It is thought that Edmonia's black grandfather, John Mike (last name unknown), escaped from slavery to Canada, where he met and married Catherine, a free-spirited Chippewa woman. From this marriage, Edmonia's mother was born.

Fearful that the government's disapproval of marriage between African Americans and Native Americans might cause trouble for Catherine's relatives, the couple moved from the Credit River Indian Reserve to a local community. "This may explain why Edmonia Lewis's parents later met in Albany and lived in Greenbush."[1]

Edmonia frequently re-created stories about her childhood. She omitted the ordinary events and instead exaggerated to impress white people with the wildness in her life. Few people knew that for a time her family lived in the North Ward of Newark, New Jersey.

Edmonia talked mostly about her mother, perhaps because she rarely saw her father.

My mother was a wild Indian . . . born in Albany, of copper color and straight black hair. . . . My father was a Negro, and a gentleman's servant. He saw and married her. . . . Mother often left her home

14

*and wandered with her people, whose habits she
could not forget, and thus, we, her children, were
brought up in the same wild manner. Until I was
twelve, I led a wandering life, fishing, swimming,
and making moccasins.*[2]

Edmonia's mother was a gifted craftswoman,
whose rich embroideries and weavings were widely
respected. Quite possibly, like other Chippewa
mothers who customarily trained their daughters, she
showed Edmonia how to make baskets and embroider
moccasins. She may have also given Edmonia her
Chippewa name, Wildfire.

Today some people question whether Wildfire was
Edmonia's true Chippewa name. They reason that the
Chippewa have always been a peaceful people who
worship nature. There is no word for "wild" in their
language. Fire, however, would have described her
vitality and sparkle.

Edmonia liked to surprise strangers, especially
those who labeled Native Americans "wild" or "sav-
age." She called herself Wildfire and the name prevails.

Edmonia was born long after Chippewa bands had
been living in the woods near the eastern Great Lakes.
In the early times, families spent six months in birch-
bark dome-shaped wigwams and six months living in

15

groups of up to 300 people, with four or five families sharing one long summer house.

They journeyed on foot, by toboggan, or in sturdy birch-bark canoes. The men caught fish year-round in fiber nets. Children and women gathered wild berries, fruits, herbs, and onions to dry and store for the winter and special celebrations. Clans planted and harvested wild rice and summer vegetables. Everyone helped collect the sweet spring maple-tree sap, which was then boiled and strained through plant-fiber cloth.

The men hunted, and the women dried or smoked the meat the men brought back. Nothing was wasted. Even bones were pounded and mixed into stews. Women sewed the dried animal skins into shirts, buckskin pants, and moccasins, trimming them with beads and appliqué, a decoration made of one material sewed onto another. Their hand-sewn moccasins were highly prized.

Edmonia's people worshiped a Supreme Spirit who they believed protected them. Having no calendar, they used the sun and the moon to guide them through the seasons. They called January Crackling Tree Moon. February became Deep Snow Moon; June, Strawberry Moon; and August, Harvest Moon.

Edmonia may have been told about religious ceremonies during which her ancestors had chanted, danced, and asked for blessings. They worked and prayed almost every day and yet also made time to play and relax.

Native American children played with stone marbles, tops, cornhusk dolls, and tiny birch-bark canoes. Edmonia may also have played with similar toys as a child. Sometimes the children practiced tribal dances while a grandfather beat out the rhythm on a drum. Like children before her, Edmonia probably heard Chippewa tales about courageous deeds and heroes, which storytellers often shared. This was also part of her Native American heritage.

Tribal life changed drastically after Europeans arrived in large numbers in the mid-1800s. The immigrants brought new diseases—measles, smallpox, flu. Having no resistance against these foreign diseases, thousands of Native Americans died.

Before Edmonia was born, the Chippewa had of necessity begun to sell their lands to lumber companies and developers. They no longer created the clothing or crafts of their ancestors. Instead, they became dependent on trade, exchanging fur pelts for food, tools, ornaments, and blankets. As the demand for furs grew, groups sometimes traveled 1,000 miles to hunt in new territories. Close-knit gatherings and celebrations of the past began to disappear.

A new government Bureau of Indian Affairs was formed, which relocated clans to small isolated reserves. Edmonia's relatives and other Chippewa became nomads, traveling into cities or into the countryside. The government set up schools where children learned to read and write and studied "American" history and English. Eventually many children forgot their Chippewa culture.

Edmonia knew the history of her people. She claimed she had slept in a wigwam. Did she also learn the dances and chant the prayers of her ancestors? No one really knows, but in later years she did say that her childhood was a happy one. When Edmonia was about nine, she and Samuel became orphans when both parents died within a year of each other.

Edmonia's mother, who had worried about her daughter's Negroid features, was afraid Edmonia might be captured by slave snatchers. Thus, before she died, she arranged for Edmonia to stay with two aunts for at least three years.

Edmonia already knew the dangers of slavery. Living close to Niagara Falls, she had seen fugitive slaves slip into Canada under cover of darkness. But among her mother's people she felt safe. Until she was 12, she worked alongside her relatives, selling baskets, embroideries, and Native American souvenirs to tourists in Buffalo, Toronto, and Niagara Falls.

Meanwhile, Samuel had attended a government school for Native American boys. About 1852 he joined thousands of people moving west. In California he became a prosperous barber and a successful gold miner.

When Samuel returned to visit his sister, he enrolled Edmonia in the New York Central College, a school in McGrawville (a village that no longer exists), and he paid her tuition. Edmonia studied for two years in this Baptist abolitionist school, which taught youngsters of all ages. While she liked being with children her own age, she did not adjust well to the school's rules.

Used to being free, Edmonia resisted the routine, the dress code, the prayers, and the strange new foods. Worse yet, she lost patience with the reading and spelling drills demanded of her. Some researchers believe that because "certain consonants—*r, f, v, x,* and *th*—are not part of the Chippewa language, which runs many syllables together,"[3] Edmonia did not speak English properly. Others insist that her speech was fine.

A rebellious and defiant child, Edmonia was labeled "wild" by her teachers. Edmonia later said that the teachers often told her, "Here is your book, the book of Nature. Come and study it." Then she added, "They could not do a thing with me."[4] This is not entirely true, however. She did leave the school with some basic reading and writing skills.

Months later Samuel persuaded Edmonia to try another school. This time he suggested Oberlin College, near Cleveland, Ohio. The idea appealed to her because she missed young companions. But Edmonia could not know how deeply the Oberlin experience would mark the rest of her life.

Chapter
2

Oberlin College and Ohio Life

Samuel Lewis chose a unique town for his sister's schooling. Oberlin was founded in 1833 by the Reverend John Jay Shipherd and Philo Penfield Stewart. The people in this religious community believed it was a sin to own another person. For that reason they committed themselves to liberty and education, and the town became a haven for escaping slaves. Two years later Oberlin College became one of the first schools of higher education to open its doors to women and black students.

Thousands of runaway slaves made the village a stopping place on the Underground Railroad. People involved in this secret system helped slaves escape from the South to the free states and Canada. They hid runaways in churches, barns, homes, and woodsheds.

The Oberlin College campus in Ohio

Some provided false-bottom wagons. Some supplied food and warm clothes. Fugitives knew they would be sheltered in Oberlin homes before being led to safety in Canada.

September 13, 1858, remains a memorable date in the town's history. On that day more than 200 Oberlin students and citizens forcibly rescued an 18-year-old slave from a United States marshal. Twenty men were jailed for defying the Federal government's enforcement of the Fugitive Slave Law.

This law demanded that a Federal marshal arrest a

runaway slave or be fined $1,000. An arrested slave or a free black could neither seek a jury trial nor defend himself or herself. People who helped escaping slaves could be jailed and also fined $1,000. Officers who caught a fugitive received a $50 fee. Oberlin became famous and gained a reputation for being a town "peculiar in [doing] that which is good."[1]

Edmonia arrived in Oberlin by stagecoach on a fall day in 1859, when she was about 15 years old. Because she did not qualify for college, she was accepted on probation in the Young Ladies Preparatory Department. With brother Samuel paying all her expenses, here she registered officially as Mary Edmonia Lewis, which is believed to be the name she was given at birth.

Mrs. Marianne F. Dascomb, who supervised the women's training, assigned Mary Edmonia to "catch-up" high school courses. A stern, pious woman, she had strict rules, which everyone obeyed.

In the first year, Mary Edmonia took classes in botany, algebra, composition, rhetoric, literature, and Bible study. For her elective she chose "linear drawing," which emphasized lines and shapes more than color. She said she wanted to draw people and things. She thought that if she had any artistic talent, it came from her mother. Edmonia probably did not realize that the years she lived with the Chippewa had already begun to train her to observe and recall fine details.

Art lessons must have delighted Mary Edmonia. For the first time she may have seen reproductions of sculptures modeled after Greek and Roman statues. One may have been the *Greek Slave,* a nude figure with draped cloth in one hand, made by the famous American sculptor Hiram Powers. Today this statue is considered one of Powers's best works.

Urania is the only drawing Mary Edmonia did that has survived from her teenage years. The woman in the sketch holds a globe, perhaps suggesting to Mary Edmonia that she, too, one day might offer something to the world. The drapery and other fine details indicate that Mary Edmonia already drew well at age 17.

Dropping the more ordinary name Mary, she signed *Urania* as Edmonia Lewis. She would use this signature the rest of her life. She gave this drawing to a favorite classmate, Clara Steele Norton, as a wedding present. Several generations later a member of Clara's family presented it to Oberlin College.

Edmonia and 11 other female students lived with the Reverend John Keep and his wife. Edmonia was the only "colored" boarder, and Mrs. Keep gave her a

Edmonia Lewis

Edmonia's talent was evident in this early drawing titled Urania.

single room on the second floor of the house.

Mr. Keep was a highly respected elder trustee on the college board. He preached, raised funds for the school, and was a father figure to his younger boarders. An abolitionist and strong supporter of women's rights, he had cast the deciding vote that opened Oberlin College to women students.

While at Oberlin, Edmonia lived in the home of the Reverend John Keep.

Enthusiastic and cheerful, Edmonia was a conscientious pupil whose grades were average. She did, however, receive an A in first-year algebra and began upper high school and some college-level liberal arts courses the following year. From 1860 to 1863 she studied Greek, French, Latin, composition, zoology, and the mechanics of writing. But she could not change one bothersome childhood habit. She spoke English awkwardly. And although she loved music, it

26

has been said that the flow of her speech and sounds made singing difficult.

She had another problem. Life among the Chippewa had been loving, natural, and direct. Having lived apart from white people for most of her early life, Edmonia was unfamiliar with and untrained in the formal manners that white society valued. Her classmates thought her behavior different and often misunderstood what she meant to say. Several girls considered her direct comments and responses curt and her style uppity. She was also well liked by many and had a good reputation, but her unpolished speech and her clumsiness did limit her social contacts somewhat.

Marianne Dascomb was a stern woman and a strict disciplinarian.

Despite these handicaps, Oberlin seemed to be a wise choice for her education. The town had a large free African American population, with about 30

27

among the college's 250 students. The school motto—"The mind and heart, not color, make the man and woman too"[2] —was reassuring.

The college let it be known that interracial contacts were up to the students. "If both agree, colored and white students walk . . ., eat . . ., and attend classes and worship together."[3] Edmonia's friends were white.

Outwardly Oberlin accepted all people. Many living in nearby towns, however, did not share Oberlin's ideals. Some people labeled Oberlin "the hotbed of abolitionists." Tolerant as the townspeople appeared to be, they were not all without prejudice. Hidden racial tensions existed in many hearts.

Possibly while Edmonia was planning for her journey to Oberlin during the summer of 1859, John Brown, a fiery abolitionist, and his small band of rebels were forming their plot to steal weapons from the United States arsenal at Harpers Ferry, Virginia (now West Virginia). After arming the local slaves, Brown expected to lead them in an uprising.

Just two months after Edmonia arrived in Oberlin, on October 16, 1859, John Brown's revolt failed. This rebellion nonetheless stirred Oberlin and the nation. Brown's father had been a founder of Oberlin College.

Two men in his band were African American Oberlin students. Everyone in Oberlin grieved when Brown and his followers were caught, tried for treason, and hanged.

During Christmas vacation, being an orphan, Edmonia remained on campus in the Keeps' care. Thus, she attended the memorial service for John Brown and the Oberlin students. At the ceremony she felt the sorrow of the mourning families and the rage that slavery aroused. She was proud of John Brown and the courage he had shown in fighting to free her father's people.

Within a few years Edmonia would honor John Brown through her developing artistic talents and share the memory of his dream with Bostonians.

Chapter 3

The Case of the Spiced Wine

"*E*xotic" is how Edmonia's peers described her. Below average height (under five feet tall), she had soft, delicate features and black, straight, coarse hair. Some people attributed her color, features, and hair to her Chippewa heritage; others, to her African American father.

Outgoing and eager, Edmonia enjoyed Oberlin until her senior year. On January 27, 1862, between semesters at the college, an incident occurred that caused a devastating scandal. It not only disrupted the surface calm of the community; it also changed Edmonia's life forever.

More than a century later, exactly what happened remains unclear. Records have disappeared, and the stories that do exist were written years after the events took place.

It is believed that two of Edmonia's close friends, Christina Ennes and Maria Miles, who also lived with the Keeps, had been taunting her. No one knows whether or not the teasing had anything to do with what happened.

What is certain is that on this day Christina and Maria had planned a lighthearted outing, a sleigh ride to Christina's home with "two gentlemen friends."

Edmonia, who was not asked to join the sleighing party, invited the girls to her room for tea and hot spiced wine, presumably a mixture of wine, allspice, and sugar. Believing the wine would keep them warm against the cold, sharp weather, Christina and Maria gladly accepted the refreshments.

When the young men, E. R. Pelton and Prentice Loomis, arrived, all dressed warmly and the full sleigh left. Their destination was Birmingham, nine miles northwest of Oberlin. Six miles into the trip, both girls suddenly complained of extreme stomach cramps and became violently ill. The men hurried the horses along, and on arrival in Birmingham, the girls were put to bed. Two local doctors, Dr. Park and Dr.

McConolly, examined and questioned Christina and Maria. The doctors surmised that the illness was caused by internal poisoning—probably by cantharides, a preparation of powdered, dried beetles known as Spanish fly.

This preparation, of ancient origin, came from southern Europe. It was considered an aphrodesiac. If used externally, it could blister and redden the skin. Internally, it could damage the kidneys and was dangerously toxic.

Despite the rule forbidding alcoholic beverages on school grounds, Edmonia apparently kept wine in her room. The girls accused her of having served them a drugged wine. The doctors also believed that Edmonia had poisoned the wine with a stimulant. Yet, one wonders how she could obtain Spanish fly in Oberlin. This question has never been answered.

News traveled fast. The issue gave enemies an opportunity to attack the ideals of the college. Villagers reacted with shock, indignation, anger, and shame.

Newspapers remained silent for two weeks. The father of one man in the sleighing party requested Edmonia's arrest, but she was not jailed. Neither Samuel Hendry, the village mayor, nor the town constables nor the college took action. Everyone was waiting to see whether the girls recovered. During their recovery, Reverend Keep questioned them and Edmonia and concluded that Edmonia was innocent. Mrs. Dascomb, however, who had enrolled Edmonia, felt under pressure from local citizens. Thus, she sought legal charges against her pupil.

Impatient people finally decided to administer their own justice. One night as Edmonia was leaving the Keep house, she was abducted, pulled into a deserted field behind the house, and severely beaten.

The village bell rang out when Edmonia was missed. Searchers hunted through the night until they found her lying unconscious in the snow, where she had been left to die. "The vigilantes were never revealed and there is no record of any action [being] taken against them."[1]

On February 11, 1862, the *Cleveland Plains* newspaper, acknowledging it did not have all the facts, nevertheless printed dramatic headlines: "Mysterious Affair at Oberlin—Suspicion of Foul Play—Two Ladies Poisoned—The Suspected One Under Arrest." The antiabolitionist staff of this paper looked forward to a trial.

The Case of the Spiced Wine

The community paper, *The Lorain County News,* edited by Henry E. Peck, a strong abolitionist and an Oberlin professor, printed its comments eight days later.

> We have hitherto refrained from speaking of the matter because we had supposed that the ends of justice would best be promoted by our silence. The people of Oberlin must see to it that the accused girl, "whose character has been exemplary, who is an orphan . . . and whose color subjects her to prejudice" [is] guaranteed the common rights of law.

While Edmonia healed slowly from her physical wounds, her friends sought the full facts. Fortunately the lawyer John Mercer Langston offered to defend her.

John Mercer Langston was an extraordinary man. In 1862, this slender, handsome Oberlin College graduate was the first and only black lawyer in Ohio. He and Edmonia shared common cultures. Born to a Virginia plantation owner and a freed slave, his mother was part Native American, part African American, and part white. And he had also been orphaned at an early age.

After his Oberlin graduation, when he found he could not enter a law school because of his color, John Langston enrolled in Oberlin again, this time in the Theology Department.

John Mercer Langston defended Edmonia at the pretrial hearing.

The Case of the Spiced Wine

After earning a master's degree, Langston read law for an antislavery judge. Then in 1854, against all Ohio customs, "he was admitted to the bar—on the polite fiction that he passed as a white man."[2]

Langston, the uncle of Lewis Leary, one of the Oberlin students who had died in the John Brown raid, lived in an all-white neighborhood and defended mostly white clients. Black men in trouble with the law rarely sought his help because they knew that being defended by another black would add to their problems. Nevertheless, Langston was proud of his heritage. Later, during the Civil War, he recruited troops for black regiments and worked hard (but unsuccessfully) in Ohio to win the right for African Americans to vote.

Many African Americans would have preferred that Edmonia be proven guilty so that the area could become peaceful again. Langston took the case in spite of these sentiments. He knew that Edmonia could be charged with murder if the girls died, but he saw loopholes in the charges against her. When the pretrial hearing was postponed to give Edmonia time to heal from her vicious beating, he left town briefly to research the medical facts. His goal was to prove insufficient evidence.

With two inexperienced justices, Daniel Bushnell and Eli B. Hawk, presiding, the hearing began on February 26, 1862. The event attracted hundreds of people—college students, villagers, friends of the ill girls, out-of-towners, as well as Edmonia's supporters. Held in a downtown business hall, the hearing lasted six days.

Mr. Chopin of Birmingham and Charles Johnston of Elyria (who was trained in medicine) were Christina's and Maria's personal lawyers. Edmonia, still recovering from her injuries, had to be helped into court. She watched the proceedings in silence.

The prosecuting attorneys called several witnesses— Maria and Christina, their young men escorts, Christina's father, students, and Dr. Park and Dr. McConolly. The doctors again testified that cantharides probably had poisoned the girls.

Langston did not call a single person. He concentrated instead on vigorously cross-examining every witness. Taking the offense, he suggested that if Edmonia had "doctored" the wine, she did so as a prank. He argued that neither Christina's or Maria's stomach residues nor their bladder contents had been analyzed or preserved. Moreover, no evidence of Spanish fly was found in Edmonia's room. He reminded everyone that no one had been murdered, and he urged that the charges be dismissed.

Mrs. Dascomb and even Reverend Keep expected the judges to believe the girls' stories. But the judges decided not to bring the case to trial. A freed Edmonia was carried from the courtroom by cheering friends.

Afterward, the conservative paper *The Plain Dealer* printed a final editorial on March 12, 1862.

The prisoner was black . . . the lawyers were black . . . and both Justices were black . . . and no white persons could enter the room but by special permission.

This mysterious episode has since become a legend. With official records of the township lost, only speculation remains.

Setting the crisis aside, the citizens and the college returned to more normal routines—spring classes, the celebration of maple syrup season, and to the national tragedy, the Civil War, which would cause young males to leave to join the Union army.

Edmonia's accusers, embarrassed by the outcome, did not return to college. Mayor Hendry was voted out of office, perhaps because he had not asked for a prompt investigation. Later he became a trustee on the Oberlin College board.

E d m o n i a   L e w i s

After the Civil War, John Mercer Langston's career soared. He became inspector for the Freeman's Bureau (1865–1869), dean of Howard University's law school (1869–1876), American minister to Haiti (1877–1885), president of a Virginia college (1886–1888), and one of the few African Americans elected to Congress in the nineteenth century (1889–1891).

And Edmonia? Refusing to hide, she ignored the nasty comments many made. She attended classes, took part in school activities, and continued to live with the Keeps, who respected her. But the emotional trauma left deep scars. After her loyal friend Clara Steele Norton married her Union army soldier fiance and left the campus, 18-year-old Edmonia felt alone.

Again, in 1863, Edmonia's reputation was attacked. This time a local art teacher, who was not on the Oberlin faculty, accused her of stealing art supplies—brushes and a picture frame. No evidence was found, but the new accusations disturbed Mrs. Dascomb.

Unable to win Oberlin faculty support for her beliefs during the earlier hearing, Mrs. Dascomb now took action without faculty discussion. No one dared argue with her. She simply did not accept Edmonia's registration for her final classes. Technically, Edmonia was not expelled. But by not permitting Edmonia to register, Mrs. Dascomb effectively prevented her from graduating.

Shamed and misjudged, Edmonia considered rejoining her Chippewa relatives. Instead, she devised a better plan. She would go to Boston, Massachusetts, where she would become an artist. (Some researchers believe she wanted to study music.) Years later in an interview, she said, "I had heard a good deal about Boston, and I thought if I went there, I should perhaps find means to learn what I wanted to know."[3]

Oberlin survived its scandal. It has continued to do dedicated work and has restored its reputation. And Edmonia Lewis, by misfortune, began a journey that would make her an outstanding American sculptor of the nineteenth century.

Chapter
4

Edmonia Lewis—Artist

*E*dmonia arrived in Boston in late winter 1863.
In awe, she wandered through city streets staring at
the massive public buildings, the decorative monu-
ments, and the statues of early American patriots.

As she ate a few dry crackers on the city hall steps,
her eyes were drawn to the front of the building and
to the largest statue she had ever seen—a life-size
figure of Benjamin Franklin, the work of Richard
Greenough.

Emotionally touched, so the story goes, Edmonia
felt a sudden urge to create a man of her own in stone.
Over the next few weeks, she returned several times to
stare at "Benjamin Franklin" for long intervals.

Her brother, Samuel, rented a small room for her in

the Studio Building, a place where artists worked. Among the notable ones were the African American landscape painter Edward Mitchell Bannister and Anne Whitney, a female sculptor who would become Edmonia's friend.

With a letter of introduction from Reverend Keep, Edmonia knocked at the door of the abolitionist William Lloyd Garrison. On learning that she hoped to sculpt, he in turn sent her to the sculptor Edward Augustus Brackett.

Brackett impressed Edmonia immediately. He had visited John Brown in jail and had taken Brown's facial measurements. Brackett then produced a portrait bust, a statue of the head, shoulders, and upper chest, of this zealous revolutionary. Edmonia later said, "A man who made a bust of John Brown must be a friend of my people."[1]

At this first meeting, Brackett handed Edmonia a lump of clay, some tools, and a plaster cast of a baby's foot. He told her, "Go home and make that; if there is anything in you, it will come out."[2]

Edmonia modeled the foot many times. Two weeks later she watched her teacher break her model into pieces to point out her mistakes. Recognizing her serious nature, Brackett gave her instruction and encouraged her to copy a plaster cast of a woman's hand.

Edmonia made her own tools and worked by trial and error until she achieved what she liked. Brackett gave this copy his approval. He also gave Edmonia a letter to a woman who bought the piece for eight dollars.

With this sum, Edmonia promptly hung a sign above the door of her studio, which read

EDMONIA LEWIS—ARTIST

One day in Brackett's studio, Edmonia "saw a broken head of [the French political writer] Voltaire among the rubbish on the floor." She asked "might [she] take it home, mend it, and try to copy it."[3]

Brackett approved of her idea because "it was a strong head." By copying, Edmonia learned another technique. Then, repeatedly, she began to shape clay into miniature relief portraits with the faces raised above the surface. She cast the better portraits in plaster and sold them at abolitionist and church meetings.

At a Watertown meeting she met Lydia Maria Child, well known for her novels and articles about women's rights, labor conditions, and the evils of slavery. Mrs. Child, aged 60, and Edmonia became friends.

When she invited Mrs. Child to see her bust of

Voltaire, Edmonia wrote the following:

> *I don't ask you because I want you to praise me. I don't know anything about sculpture yet; and it will not be good for me to be praised just because I am a colored girl. I want you to point out the faults, for that will help me learn.*[4]

But Mrs. Child thought that Edmonia had improved Voltaire's face. She had given him a warm expression, as though he were smiling within, and Mrs. Child liked what she saw. She said, "I *must* praise you, for this is extremely well done. I see you have not copied the sneering expression of the mouth. . . ."

"I did not like that expression," Edmonia replied, "and I don't suppose he always sneered."[5] She explained to Mrs. Child that Garibaldi, a Boston plaster worker, had done the plaster cast of Voltaire free of charge just because he liked what she had created.

Later, with Brackett's permission, Edmonia kept his bust of John Brown nearby as she worked on a portrait medallion of John Brown's face. On January 29, 1864, she boldly placed an advertisement in *The Liberator*, inviting the public to see her first independent sculpture at the Tremont Studio. On February 19, 1864, Lydia Child wrote an article about Edmonia, which emphasized her childhood with the

Chippewa and her lessons with Brackett, and her sales increased. In 1864 and 1865, Boston city directories listed Edmonia as a "sculptress."

Critics liked the John Brown medallion. Edmonia began to sell copies of it along with small busts of other antislavery leaders. Among them were the Massachusetts senator Charles Sumner, a lawyer who argued for universal education regardless of color or religion; Wendell Phillips, who protested proslavery laws; and of course, William Lloyd Garrison.

Proud of her Native American heritage, Edmonia respected the fact that even in the worst of times, the Chippewa had not become slaves. Now, living among social reformers, who worked to bring about liberty and justice for all, she sought freedom for her father's people. During this period, Edmonia created a small statue of a wounded black Civil War soldier saving the American flag. This statue has since been lost.

On May 28, 1863, Edmonia witnessed history in the making, first hand. The country was in the middle of the Civil War, and the Union army needed more men. On this day, Edmonia watched the young white commander Colonel Robert Gould Shaw lead the parade of the 54th Massachusetts Volunteer Infantry (the first black regiment in the North) through Boston streets to the port. Twenty-one of the soldiers had been recruited by John Mercer Langston, and Edmonia knew some of them. Police were there to prevent trouble in case the crowd became angry at the sight of an all-black troop. Instead people cared.

Amid flying flags and banners, a soldier carried one white silk banner high. It had been presented to the troop by the Colored Ladies Relief Society, and its words, "Liberty, Loyalty, and Unity," reflected the mood of the day. Six weeks later Colonel Shaw and most of his 257 men died in heavy combat at Fort Wagner, South Carolina.

Soon afterward, Edmonia asked Lydia Child for a photograph of the Colonel because she wanted to produce a portrait bust of him. Mrs. Child, who knew the Shaw family, refused and advised against the project. To a friend she wrote that she did not want "practice hands tried on his likeness." Complaining, she said:

> *[Edmonia] does not take time; she is too much in a hurry . . . without taking the intermediate steps. I do not think this is so much self-conceit, as it is an uneasy feeling . . . of making things to sell in order to pay for her daily bread. Then you must remember YOUTH . . . naturally thinks itself capable of doing anything.*[6]

Understanding that being both black and a woman put Edmonia at a terrible disadvantage, Mrs. Child suggested that Edmonia take an ordinary job to earn money to pay for professional training.

Edmonia dismissed this idea. She feared that if she were sidetracked from her goal she would not become a recognized artist. Except for her few lessons with Brackett, she remained untrained. But she had a big heart, strong hands, and determination. She cared nothing about clothes, good furniture, or fine food. Having had a Chippewa upbringing, she could live simply and manage. She fully expected to make Colonel Shaw's bust.

From memory and a photo borrowed from elsewhere, and with tips on how to handle clay from her friend Anne Whitney, Edmonia began her strenuous labor of love. Months later she cast the Shaw bust in plaster.

Lydia Child was "agreeably surprised." She was glad that Edmonia had shown Shaw as a "gentleman." She wrote that Edmonia "had succeeded so well that those familiar with the photographs of the young hero could not fail to recognize the bust. It has some imperfections as the work of beginners must necessarily have, but it was quite remarkable. . . ."[7]

*One of Edmonia's earliest works was a bust
of Colonel Robert Gould Shaw.*

Edmonia told her that as she worked, feeling his presence in the room, she had "kissed the clay." The Shaw family, too, approved the "reasonable likeness" she achieved and bought the bust.

Most important, they gave her permission to sell 100 plaster copies at the November 1864 Soldiers' Relief Fund Fair. African American artist Edward Bannister, the organizer of the fair's decorations, gave Edmonia a prominent place for her display.

Around this time Lydia Child introduced Edmonia to Harriet Hosmer. Hosmer, a young American sculptor living in Rome, was touring with her *Zenobia*, a seven-foot-tall statue of the Greek queen. When she saw Edmonia's Colonel Shaw, she thought it was finely molded and mentioned that Rome, Italy, was a haven for women artists, especially for sculptors.

In this same year (1864), Anna Quincy Waterston honored Robert Gould Shaw and Edmonia in a poem. Highlighting Edmonia's heritage and Shaw's courage, her words awakened the public's curiosity. She wrote:

> *She hath wrought well with her unpracticed hand,*
> *The mirror of her thought reflected clear*
> *This youthful hero-martyr of our land.*
> *With touch harmonious she has moulded here*
> *A memory and a prophecy—both dear: . . .*

A leader for all time in Freedom's chivalry;
The prophecy of that wide, wholesome cure
For foul distrust and bitter, cruel wrong,
Which he did give up his life to secure.
'Tis fitting that a daughter of the race
Whose chains are breaking should receive a gift
So rare as genius. Neither power nor place,
Fashion or wealth, pride, custom, caste nor hue
Can arrogantly claim what God doth lift
Above these chances and bestows on few.[8]

Edmonia became more widely known and was accepted into Boston's circle of abolitionists and those who promoted the arts. The success of the Shaw bust expanded her dreams. Bostonians, however, were amazed at her goal. A black sculptor in Rome. Indeed!

Even some abolitionists could not accept the fact that African Americans were intelligent enough to contribute to the arts. Most people were not yet acquainted with Africa's cultural history, nor did they recognize the ability that West Africans carried within when they arrived as slaves in the New World. People were unaware of West African artisans who for centuries had crafted religious masks, doors, furniture, and metal and clay tools. This heritage, which had lain quietly within, now began to surface among slaves and free blacks. Self-taught or trained as apprentices in America, many men had become skilled blacksmiths, silversmiths, chairmakers, cabinetmakers, weavers, and basketmakers. Many women worked as milliners and dressmakers.

But few Americans had heard of Neptune Thurston's carved wooden wine casket or of Phillis Wheatley's book of poetry published in England in 1773 or of the artist Scipio Moorhead, who designed the book's frontispiece. Only later in the nineteenth century would Joshua Johnson, Robert Duncanson, Edward Bannister, Henry Ossawa Tanner, and other black artists receive some recognition.

Edmonia trusted no one. She did not want pity, and so she did not share her hurtful Oberlin experience with anyone. She strove only to be worthy and to prove her talent. She wanted to be respected as a working artist. Instead people admired her as a "poor waif," a naive "Indian," or a "colored girl." Edmonia, by her actions, contradicted all stereotypes—the preconceived ideas of what people expected from a woman with her background.

Ready for a change, she thought about going to Rome. It may have been her brother, Samuel, who had traveled in Europe and the West Indies, or Harriet Hosmer's words that encouraged her. Whatever it was, with money earned from the sales of the Shaw busts, along with contributions from Samuel and several patrons who supported artists, Edmonia booked passage to Europe.

Before sailing she paid a last visit to Lydia Child. Here she glimpsed a hurtful surprise—a book that included four photographs of Colonel Shaw was on display along with one of her Shaw busts. To Edmonia's dismay, Lydia Child had sawed the lower chest away to, in her opinion, give the figure a stronger military appearance.

Hiding her feelings, Edmonia asked, "Why didn't you suggest this before I finished it?" Then graciously she added, "How much you improved it."[9]

Worried about Edmonia's management of money, Child cautioned Edmonia to earn an income as a decorative worker in plaster, and not to carve any sculptures in marble until she or someone else had paid for the expensive material.

Lydia Maria Child once said that Edmonia had an unbendable spirit. She "could cut through the heart of the Alps with a penknife." In a sense she was right.[10]

Edmonia was destined to go forward. She would chisel in marble and know that indescribable moment when she made time stand still.

Chapter 5

Awakening in Rome

*E*dmonia sailed for Europe on August 19, 1865. She stopped briefly in London and Paris to visit the abolitionist communities and then traveled to elegant Florence. Here she marveled at Michelangelo's 17-foot-tall *David* and powerful sculptures by many other Italian masters. With a letter of introduction, she met Hiram Powers, the famous American sculptor and the creator of *Greek Slave*.

Powers, also from a poor family, gave her some tools and invited her to his studio. She watched how he modeled in clay and assembled large armatures, the frameworks that supported the clay and other materials. She observed how stone cutters marked up a block of marble, using a device similar to a large compass. The points marked became a guide to enlarging small models to life-size proportions. From her observations she learned much. Then—Rome at last!

This dream city of architectural splendor, with its many piazzas—open public squares, decorative fountains, colossal statues, and museums filled with fine Greek and Roman sculptures and paintings, was what attracted artists, writers, tourists, the wealthy—and Edmonia.

Rome dazzled her. "I thought I knew everything when I came," she said. "But I soon found out I had everything to learn."[1]

In a letter to Lydia Maria Child, Edmonia wrote:

It would have done your heart good to see the warm welcome I received. . . . [Harriet Hosmer] held my hand [and made] such a neat little speech. . . . She since has called on me and we meet often.[2]

Members of the international community, which included people from many countries living in Rome, worked and socialized among themselves. Wealthy patrons who supported the arts, and well-known artists and writers met at dinner parties, picnics, amateur plays, and the popular Cafe Greco.

Through Harriet Hosmer (nicknamed Hatty), Edmonia met the American Shakespearean actress Charlotte Cushman. Liking Edmonia's independent

*Harriet Hosmer welcomed Edmonia to Rome
and introduced her to the art community.*

spirit and wanting to help, she arranged for Edmonia to rent a part of the former studio of the great Italian sculptor Antonio Canova (1757–1822).

The studio was located on Via San Niccolio di Tolentino in the center of where the international group lived. Edmonia lived a quick walk away from Plaza Barberini and the Spanish Steps, and the nearby studios of Harriet Hosmer and William Wetmore Story.

Awakening in Rome

Hatty Hosmer and Anne Whitney, who now lived in Rome, introduced Edmonia to their circle of friends. As a newcomer with a different heritage, Edmonia was a mysterious curiosity, and so received invitations to many social gatherings. The celebrated writers Elizabeth Barrett and Robert Browning, Nathaniel Hawthorne and Henry James, and American sculptor William Wetmore Story must have met Edmonia because they mentioned her in their writings.

Edmonia adapted rapidly to Rome's rhythms—busy morning and afternoon hours of work, midday siestas, walks through well-kept gardens, and early evenings on quiet streets, before they filled with strollers and cafe sitters. She learned to speak Italian better than she spoke English, and she began to wear practical clothes—loose long-sleeved blouses and wide, ruffled skirts, which freed her body for the difficult tasks she had to handle.

Rome was affordable. Living costs were low. Skilled labor could be had cheaply, and Carrara marble, the finest, least flawed marble in the world, was available in abundance. In the museums Edmonia spent weeks studying and copying classical statues, and her sculpture techniques improved.

Still, money was a problem. Even though Samuel

In 1870 when Edmonia visited Chicago, she posed for the only photos that exist of her today. The shawl she is wearing here is a photographer's prop.

sent small sums, Edmonia expected to pay her own way. She reasoned that art-buying travelers could become potential customers of the small pieces and portrait busts she hoped to produce.

Edmonia arrived in Italy when Rome was the center of neoclassical sculpture. Artists, following strict rules, were imitating historic Greek and Roman figures from past centuries. They emphasized drapery—cloths or clothing arranged in folds—and gave their figures a placid, unemotional beauty. Most statues looked similar, and their form soon influenced the furniture, fabrics, clothes, and even ladies' hairstyles of the times.

Eagerly Edmonia started her first large statue. The American Civil War was over, and she was living in Europe. Yet she turned to her African American roots, choosing to produce an imagined moment in the life of a slave. Her statue *A Freed Woman and Her Child* (1866) told a clear story.

Originally titled *Freedwoman on First Hearing of Her Liberty*, the statue portrayed a child clinging to his mother as she, on bended knees, thanks the Lord for her glorious freedom. Her hands are in chains, and a turban, the normal headdress of a slave, covers her hair. Little is known about this work because it has been lost.

Edmonia later said the piece was a "humble one." It expressed her desire to do good in a small way for her father's people. Most sculptors hired workmen to transfer figures from smaller clay or plaster models to larger marble figures. But Edmonia, wanting people to value her work as completely *original*, labored entirely alone.

Soon after completing *A Freed Woman and Her Child*, Edmonia modeled a portrait bust of Anna Quincy Waterston (1866). She was the wife of the Reverend Robert C. Waterston and the poet whose poem had honored Colonel Robert Gould Shaw and Edmonia. The Waterstons had collected funds for Edmonia's first purchases of Italian marble. Although Edmonia created mostly busts of men, she may have done this one in appreciation for the Waterstons' support. Finely chiseled, a delicate lace collar beneath Anna Quincy Waterston's gentle face with just a hint of a smile projects a sense of the poet's modesty.

A year later, finally at Shaw's sister's request, Edmonia created the bust of the colonel in marble, and the family bought it. Next she produced a grouping of two half-life-size figures, and this statue, *Forever Free* (1867), brought her instant recognition and vast applause. Originally known as *The Morning of Liberty*, it was the first statue to celebrate the Emancipation

*Edmonia modeled this bust of poet
Anna Quincy Waterston in 1866.*

Proclamation. With this document, on January 1,
1863, Abraham Lincoln had declared all slaves living
in rebelling states forever free. Later when Congress
passed the Thirteenth Amendment (January 31,
1865), slavery was no longer legal anywhere in the
United States.

Forever Free *celebrated the
Emancipation Proclamation.*

Forever Free was the first statue of an African American family. Again Edmonia's kneeling slave woman is thanking God for her delivery from bondage. The man stands tall. A broken chain is wrapped around his upraised forearm. His other arm comforts the woman. The man's pose is similar to that of a Greek sculpture *(Laocoon)* in the Vatican Museum. The woman's pose was inspired by an abolitionist emblem entitled "Am I not a woman and a sister?" The couple seem dazed, as though not totally understanding that the Emancipation Proclamation had declared them forever free.

People were attracted to the expressions of gratitude and wonderment on the faces. Surprisingly, except for the man's thick, curly hair, the couple did not resemble African Americans. A few critics thought their limbs awkward and not well proportioned.

When Edmonia unveiled her sculpture of human beings who exposed deep emotions during a momentous experience in their lives, she broke with conventional art of the time. Her style was fresh, her subjects believable. This statue indicated changes to come in neoclassical sculpture. Edmonia had also fulfilled her Boston wish. She had made a man, and a woman, too, in stone.

Sometimes Edmonia hired stonecutters to help produce her larger figures. She now borrowed $800 to have her *Forever Free* figures executed in marble. Then she shipped the statue, along with the bills for materials and shipping costs, to the abolitionist lawyer Samuel E. Sewall in Boston. The statue's unexpected arrival shocked the abolitionists. Although Sewall had not commissioned, or given an order for, the work, he paid a customs duty of $200 to prevent its being auctioned off.

In a letter to Maria Weston Chapman, aide to William Lloyd Garrison, on February 5, 1867, Edmonia wrote: "I will not take anything for my labor. Mr. Garrison has given his whole life for my father's people, and I think I might give him a few months [of my] work."[3] She did seek costs however, of $1,000, but added she would contribute $200 from money she had received from a Mr. Loring and a Mr. Bowditch before she left Boston.

In a second letter she wrote: "Will you be so kind as to let me know what has become of it [*Forever Free*]? . . . I am in great need of the money. The statue represents two years work. . . ."[4] Then, worried that people might believe that if they helped, she would become spoiled, she assured Mrs. Chapman that the donors would really be caring "for one who has given all for poor humanity. . . ." She added, "Unless I receive the money, I will not be able to get on this year."[5]

Sewall and Garrison took responsibility for collecting donations—a dollar here, five dollars there, whatever one could afford. The funds accumulated slowly. Several years later they would present *Forever Free* to the Reverend Leonard Grimes, pastor of the 12th Street Baptist Chruch. During the years of slavery he had smuggled slaves from a Virginia plantation.

In the late 1860s and through the next decade, Edmonia Lewis reached the height of her popularity. She produced and sold more than 24 outstanding statues and received people in her Rome studio from many parts of the world.

Chapter 6

Edmonia Meets Henry Wadsworth Longfellow

*T*ourists traveling through Europe found their way easily to Edmonia's popular studio. From the listings in Rome's guidebooks, they learned where and when she opened her door. Imposing on her time, they came to satisfy themselves that this small woman with small hands could sculpt, and do it well. After they watched Edmonia knead and ready the clay or chisel, grind, and polish the marble, some visitors became patrons.

It was fashionable at the time for the wealthy to decorate their formal living rooms with sculpture. Visiting British and Americans often left Edmonia orders for original busts, which might be delivered months or years later. The less wealthy bought small copies of classical museum statues.

Edmonia Meets Henry Wadsworth Longfellow

When her finances were low, Edmonia did every-thing herself—the modeling in clay, the plaster casts, and when she found a buyer, the final conversion to marble. During the height of the profitable years, Edmonia kept nine male assistants busy. They made plaster casts from her clay sculptures. They also marked up the marble and carved and polished the hands, feet, and draperies. Why males? In the mid-1800s, society designated sculpture as an art form reserved for men. Women were not trained as stonecutters.

Edmonia still trusted no one and consequently had no close friends. Uncomfortable among the gossipy group of international artists, where everything she did was noticed, she felt compelled to prove that African Americans and Native Americans were capable human beings.

She did, nevertheless, receive almost all visitors cordially. However, Anne Whitney, who liked Edmonia's forthright behavior, once watched her order a Southerner out of her studio. She resented his sister's refusal to sign the guest book of a black artist.

Anne Whitney's and Edmonia's backgrounds were quite different, and although not best friends, they liked each other. Anne Whitney came from an educated family, whose ancestors had settled in America in

1635. She had been a teacher and a poet before becoming a sculptor, after the age of 30. She completed many commissions between her fiftieth and eightieth birthdays. Like Edmonia, she socialized very little in the art community.

Anne Whitney had conflicting feelings about Edmonia's talent. She did suggest gently a need for professional training, but she also accepted Edmonia's refusal of all advice. Sometimes they shared tea or supper.

Edmonia does not seem to have practiced a specific religion. Yet, after a hard day's work, she often sought rest in St. Peter's Church. Listening to vesper chants in the late afternoon and thinking about sculptural problems, she watched the sun's rays flicker on church walls and felt more at peace. She was the only black person there, and the curious priests welcomed her.

Whether because the priests were friendly or because she had inner yearnings, Edmonia was soon attracted to Catholicism. Some historians, knowing Edmonia was named Mary as a child, believe she returned to the faith of her childhood. Others conclude she joined the Catholic Church for the first time in Rome. Regardless of the theories, Edmonia practiced Catholicism in her own unique way. Once when she returned from Paris and learned that her neighbors were dying of cholera during an epidemic, she put a Bible and a bottle of brandy near her bed. She said that if one gave out, she could take comfort in the other.

Sometime after she became an active Catholic, Edmonia designed *Madonna Holding the Christ Child.* This altarpiece included two angels at the Madonna's feet. During its construction, Cardinal Pecci introduced Edmonia to a Scotsman, the wealthy Marquis de Bute. He, too, was an orphan and a recent Catholic convert. A landowner and a scholar, he bought the altarpiece for either $2,000 or $3,000—but not before Pope Pius IX visited the studio and blessed Edmonia's work-in-progress.

This purchase relieved Edmonia of financial worries, and the Pope's visit restored her energy. She forever considered the Pope's presence one of the highlights of her life.

Living among artists, Edmonia created almost constantly. After completing *Forever Free*, she began major projects that arose out of heartfelt remembrances—her early life among the Chippewa and the unforgettable anguish she had experienced at Oberlin College. They would become her finest works and would keep her occupied for several years.

Beginning in 1868, 24-year-old Edmonia made several versions of *Hagar*, also known as *Hagar in the Wilderness*. About the same time, she began groupings and busts inspired by Henry Wadsworth Longfellow's poem *The Song of Hiawatha* and also started a bust of the poet himself. Hagar had interested Edmonia for a long time. She may have heard about Hagar in Oberlin or after she began to practice Catholicism. According to the Old Testament, Hagar was a young Egyptian servant to Abraham's wife, Sarah. (In the mid-1800s, Egyptians were considered incorrectly by many to be black Africans.) After Hagar bore a son by Abraham, a jealous Sarah sent her and her boy, Ishmael, into the wilderness to survive alone.

Edmonia portrayed her 52-inch *Hagar* as a courageous, graceful maiden, whose upturned face looks skyward. Her hands are clasped in prayer. Her son, too young to know his mother's fears, is unseen. The empty jug lying at her feet perhaps symbolizes how desperate their journey was. Edmonia gave Hagar smooth skin, wavy hair, and a brow furrowed in pain. Again, Edmonia blended natural emotions with the popular neoclassical style.

Hagar appears to be in motion, ready to step forward. Is she pleading for God's mercy or for help? Is she

listening to an angel ask, "What troubles thee, Hagar?"

Edmonia identified personally with Hagar. She had left relatives behind to go to Oberlin, then on to Boston, and finally to Rome. Over the years she had become an outcast in Oberlin, a stranger in Boston, and the "Negress" among Rome's artists. The sculpture *Hagar* reveals Edmonia's sensitivity to the homeless and the difficulties Hagar endured. Repeatedly, she said, "I have strong sympathy for all women who have struggled and suffered."[1]

Unfortunately, most people did not understand Edmonia's message. Lydia Child saw Hagar as a heavy-hipped, stout woman, and Anne Whitney thought the statue should not have been made in marble. But opinions have changed.

Today *Hagar* is thought to be one of Edmonia's most important works. Standing boldly on a base in the National Museum of American Art in Washington, D.C., *Hagar* has become an American treasure. The timeless sentiments portrayed in marble speak as strongly for modern women as they did for women who had limited freedom more than a century ago.

About the time that Edmonia created *Forever Free*, she began to focus on her Native American ancestors. Having read Longfellow's *The Song of Hiawatha*,

Edmonia's sympathy for women who have struggled and suffered is evident in her sculpture Hagar.

based on Native American legends, Edmonia made the poet her hero.

Henry Wadsworth Longfellow, born in 1807 into a comfortable family of English ancestry, became a famous poet and a pioneer in his own time. A graduate of Bowdoin College in Maine, he was skilled in languages. Besides English, Longfellow spoke French, Spanish, Italian, a little German, Danish, and Finnish.

Before daring to support his family as a poet, he taught at Bowdoin and later at Harvard University. Though not an abolitionist, Longfellow spoke out against slavery. He told audiences: "If you were a slave, the thing you would wish for most of all would be your freedom."[2]

Longfellow's deep interest in Native Americans dated back to 1823, but he did not start his poem about Hiawatha until 1854. When he began, joyously he wrote: "If I had one hundred hands, I would keep them busy with 'Hiawatha.' Nothing ever absorbed me more."[3]

In the poem, Hiawatha's Chippewa tribal elders told him to marry a useful, skilled woman whose "heart and hand moved together." Longfellow chose to unite the Chippewa with the Dakota, a tribe with a reputation for fierceness. Perhaps he thought such a marriage might heal the wounds between tribes and that they could begin to live in peace together.

The romantic *Song of Hiawatha*, which interwove facts with fiction, became one of the most popular books of the nineteenth century. It appealed to thousands who liked to imagine what it might be like to survive in the wilderness.

While some people greatly admired it, others sneered at the Hiawatha epic. Nonetheless, Longfellow's poem awakened people to the beauty and the plight of Native American life. Thereafter several generations of American schoolchildren had to memorize portions of the poem.

Longfellow's narrative poem inspired Edmonia to create at least four works between 1866 and 1872. In *The Wooing of Hiawatha* (1866), better known as *The Old Arrowmaker and His Daughter*, Minnehaha sits sewing moccasins, a task Edmonia claimed she did as a child. In *The Marriage of Hiawatha* (1866–1867), Minnehaha and Hiawatha stand side by side, symbolizing the union of two tribes, the Chippewa and Dakota. Since the Civil War had ended, Edmonia may also have been expressing hope that Northern and Southern Americans would put aside their differences and work instead to heal the nation. Two smaller busts of the

Hiawatha   *Minnehaha*

characters, *Hiawatha* and *Minnehaha* (completed 1868) were produced in the traditional neoclassical style.

The Old Arrowmaker and His Daughter so impressed Charlotte Cushman that she raised funds to purchase the marble, added her own money, and gave the statue to Boston's YMCA as a gift. She hoped the YMCA would then buy *The Marriage of Hiawatha*, but this did not happen.

Edmonia created at least three separate groupings of *The Old Arrowmaker and His Daughter* between 1866 and 1872. Each one, delicately refined in marble and less than two feet high, illustrates a moment that

The Marriage of Hiawatha *is one of Edmonia Lewis's most recently rediscovered statues. The story of its journey is still unknown.*

Edmonia Meets Henry Wadsworth Longfellow

Longfellow described in his poem:

At the doorway of his wigwam
Sat the ancient Arrow-maker,
In the land of the Dacohtas,
Making arrow-heads of jasper.
Arrow-heads of chalcedony.
At his side, in all her beauty,
Sat the lovely Minnehaha,
Sat his daughter, Laughing Water.
Plaiting mats of flags and rushes,
Of the past the old man's thoughts were,
And the maiden's of the future.
. . . .
Through their thoughts they heard a footstep,
Heard a rustling in the branches,
And with glowing cheek and forehead
With the deer upon his shoulders
Suddenly from out the woodlands
Hiawatha stood before them.
. . . .
At the feet of Laughing Water
Hiawatha laid his burden,
Threw the red deer from his shoulders;
And the maiden looked up at him,
Looked up from her mat of rushes,
Said with gentle look and accent,
"You are welcome, Hiawatha!"
. . . .

76

The Old Arrowmaker and His Daughter
was inspired by Longfellow's poem
The Song of Hiawatha.

Edmonia Meets Henry Wadsworth Longfellow

The scene Edmonia chose to sculpt may appear simply to show two Native Americans, a young woman and an old man, doing tasks together. Yet on closer look a story unfolds.

The old arrowmaker interrupts his task to gaze up and greet an unseen person (Hiawatha). Minnehaha sits quietly by her father, a mat of woven plant rushes covering her knees. Looking up, she sees and welcomes the stranger.

Hiawatha has just laid a roebuck, a small deer with stumpy horns, native to Europe, at their feet. The gift of the deer indicates Hiawatha's wish for permission to court his future bride.

Why Longfellow chose a roebuck is unclear. But, living in Europe, Edmonia must have known about this animal. Its size fits her composition well.

If you were to stand in front of the arrowmaker, you would be exactly where Hiawatha presented his gift. Looking directly into the arrowmaker's eyes, you might sense the father's feelings: Perhaps Hiawatha would protect his daughter. The arrowmaker may be about to grant the stranger's request.

To the touch, the arrowmaker's forward leg feels like velvety flesh. In contrast, Minnehaha's bumpy, greyish-white mat is rougher to the hand. Edmonia, idealizing Minnehaha, gave her a classical European face. Only the headdress and clothes hint at her Native American culture. The wrinkles under the arrowmaker's eyes add maturity to his face, and his hair and firm nose suggest traits often thought to belong to Native Americans.

Edmonia, again breaking with the popular art style, varied the textures and shades of the white marble. Every article is realistic, from the shell necklace strung on corded fiber rope to the fur skins and the tools the figures are using. By presenting father and daughter with dignity and respect, Edmonia displayed the nobility of her people.

In the winter of 1868–1869, Edmonia began to work on a portrait bust of Henry Wadsworth Longfellow. After she learned that the writer and his family were staying at the Costanzi Hotel in Rome, she deliberately set out to shadow him. Longfellow was now a famous man. But undaunted by his celebrity, Edmonia followed him as he walked about the city. Glimpsing him from a distance, she crossed in front of him or headed him off on a street corner. Then back in the studio, she worked from memory to capture his features.

One day Longfellow's brother Samuel visited

Edmonia's studio. He thought her portrait likeness decent and soon returned with the rest of the family. Only the nose looked wrong, so Longfellow obligingly posed for one sitting.

Afterward the poet's family and his close friends agreed that Edmonia had caught a special expression. And Longfellow felt Edmonia had made one of the best likenesses he had ever seen. This was a great tribute considering that both Hiram Powers and the less experienced Edmonia made portrait busts of Longfellow within a month of each other.

A merchant in Liverpool, England, ordered the bust, which was completed in 1871. Influential friends bought a copy for Harvard University, where over the years it has been displayed or stored in several places. Since 1987, when it is not on loan, Edmonia's bust of Longfellow may be seen in Harvard's art museum.

Courageously Edmonia had pursued her hero and finally managed to meet him. And what she produced became greater than she had dreamed possible. Longfellow admired her work. But sad to say, after that one time together, the poet and the sculptor never met again.

Henry Wadsworth Longfellow

Chapter
7

Travels and "Fancy Pieces"

*B*eginning in 1868 and into the next decade, Edmonia made several ocean crossings to the United States. Always she brought crated sculptures with her. The fastest known ship at the time was the British Cunard Line's *Persia,* which took a minimum of 16 days from Rome. Since all vessels lacked twentieth-century comforts, Edmonia needed a strong stomach to survive her sea voyages.

On each trip she stopped in American cities, where she stayed with abolitionist friends and met again tourists who had become clients after visiting her studio. As her reputation as an artist grew, she became an honored guest in Boston, New York, Philadelphia, Chicago, and San Francisco.

Edmonia was a wise businesswoman. She sought orders for sculptures wherever she went. She would have preferred to produce works based on literature and history, but realizing that sweet, sentimental subjects appealed to the public, she also created at least three statues of innocent cherubs. Today these figures are called her "fancy pieces."

In 1870 Edmonia brought *Hagar* to the United States. In Chicago she met John Jones, the wealthy black owner of the city's major dry-cleaning business. He was well known among the abolitionists, and his house guests had included William Lloyd Garrison and Frederick Douglass.

Taking charge of Edmonia's visit, he introduced *Hagar* to the city's citizens with a front-page advertisement in the *Chicago Tribune*. He may also have advised Edmonia to exhibit the statue publicly, because in August 1870, Edmonia placed her own personal ad in the *Tribune*. Calling herself "the young and gifted colored sculptress from Rome," she invited the public to view *Hagar* in Chicago's largest meeting place, Farwell Hall. The 25-cent admission also included the cost of a raffle ticket for the sculpture.

Edmonia later told Anne Whitney that she had collected $6,000 for the statue. The published sale price was $3,000. Since society did not expect women to advance their careers publicly, Edmonia's action must have astonished people. But she was a survivor, and her self-promotion paved the way for future black artists to advertise and to introduce Americans to their talents.

On one of her early trips, either in 1869 or 1870, Edmonia met Dr. Harriot Hunt, Boston's first woman physician. Dr. Hunt, seriously ill with kidney disease, wanted a memorial monument of Hygieia, the Greek goddess of health, to grace her grave. She commissioned Edmonia to produce a life-size statue in marble. When Dr. Hunt died, in 1875, Edmonia's *Hygieia* (1874) was placed on the grave in Mount Auburn Cemetary in Cambridge, Massachusetts.

For more than 100 years, the statue has endured harsh outdoor weather—ice, hail, snow, air pollution, and strong sunlight. Today its marble is pocked and roughened, and parts of *Hygieia*'s face and the decorations on the base have worn away. In 1995 a rescue committee launched a fund-raising project to repair the damages and prevent further destruction. The statue may have to be preserved under glass with special ventilation to protect it against nature's tough elements.

Although it was unusual at that time for a woman

to travel alone, in August 1873 Edmonia traveled west by rail. She took with her five statues: *The Marriage of Hiawatha, Asleep, Awake, Poor Cupid,* and a second bust of *Lincoln*—all together about 2,000 pounds of marble.

Anne Whitney thought that Edmonia had undertaken this difficult, lonely, cross-country trip because she hoped to see her brother again. Unfortunately Edmonia and Samuel did not meet.

Edmonia considered Samuel her most loyal supporter, and they corresponded frequently. After Samuel sent Edmonia to Oberlin, he went off on an adventurous life of his own. He worked as a barber in San Francisco before moving to Sierra County in California, where he also became a miner. While recuperating from an illness, he toured Europe and the West Indies for two years, and on his return he lived briefly in Portland, Oregon, and later in Idaho City. After his barber shop burned down, he settled in Elk Creek, Montana. Finally, in 1870, he moved to Bozeman, Montana, where he built a new shop, which became quite popular.

In Bozeman, Samuel was active in community affairs and became one of the young city's leading citizens. He also constructed several small rental cottages and became known as "the colored barber." Townspeople respected him highly. They said he was "a man of indefatigable industry, excellent judgment, and refined tastes. . . ." Meaning it as a compliment, they considered him "physically, intellectually, and socially . . . a white man."[1]

Between 1881 and 1883, Samuel built a large brick home with fine shade trees for himself. In 1883 he married Melissa Railey Bruce, a widow with four children, and a fifth child, a son, was born to them.

Instead of hearing the news from her brother, Edmonia learned of Samuel's marriage from her aunts.

Samuel Lewis's home in Bozeman, Montana

She was, of course, hurt that he did not share this news directly with her. They did keep in touch after the marriage, but whether they ever saw each other again is still unknown. (Samuel died in 1896 after a brief, painful illness.)

Other events, however, did bring Edmonia some joy. Edmonia told reporters she had statues to sell, and she had come west because she believed San Franciscans and Westerners were "more liberal." About 150 people, blacks and whites, came to her opening in the Pine Street San Francisco Art

87

Association Exhibition Hall. *Poor Cupid* and *The Marriage of Hiawatha* sold immediately.

Poor Cupid (1873), also known as *Cupid Caught in a Trap* or *Ensnared by Love*, shows a winged cupid with bow and arrow and quiver strapped to his back. It is done in typical neoclassical style. As he reaches to pick up a rose, Cupid's foot releases a trap. Was Edmonia revealing personal feelings? Could Cupid also be ensnared, or trapped, by love? A San Francisco paper had reported her engaged to be married. If true, nothing seemed to have come of it.

Newspaper reviews of the exhibition were mixed. On August 30, 1873, the *Pacific Appeal* described Edmonia as "a very intelligent lady." A week later the paper announced that *Asleep* and *Awake* had won a gold medal from the Academy of Arts and Science in Naples, Italy. *The Elevator* compared Edmonia's work to that of Hiram Powers. *The Chronicle* said her pieces showed "considerable artistic taste," but the critic also thought she had overworked the chisel. Another reviewer thought that the pieces were too small and overpolished. This critic may not have known that neoclassical sculptors usually finished works with a smoothly polished surface.

After the exhibit closed, Edmonia moved the remaining statues to San Jose, California. There her exhibit competed with 100 paintings being shown at the same time in the City Hall Market. To attract crowds, Edmonia displayed her work in a wigwamlike booth and reduced the admission from 50 cents to a quarter. More than 1,600 people came to see her work.

Poor Cupid *was one of the statues Edmonia brought with her to the United States in 1873.*

Sarah Knox-Goodrich, who had come to California in a wagon train, was a wealthy San Jose citizen and a crusader for women's rights. She bought *Asleep* and *Awake* and eventually presented the statues to the San Jose Public Library. When the African American community decided to honor Edmonia with a reception, she asked instead that they buy *Abraham Lincoln*. That would please her more. She sailed back to Italy on January 13, 1874, satisfied knowing that the Friends of the Library had committed themselves to purchasing this statue through subscriptions.

Twenty-four years after Edmonia's statues were

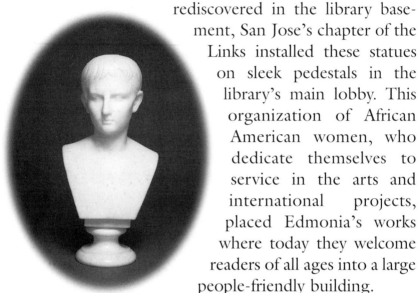

Edmonia Lewis's
Young Octavian

rediscovered in the library base-ment, San Jose's chapter of the Links installed these statues on sleek pedestals in the library's main lobby. This organization of African American women, who dedicate themselves to service in the arts and international projects, placed Edmonia's works where today they welcome readers of all ages into a large people-friendly building.

Over the years Edmonia con-tinued to copy Rome's classical statues. One commission, *Young Octavian* (1873), also known as *Augustus* (Rome's emperor from 27 B.C. to A.D. 14), today is considered an exceptional copy of the classical work.

Edmonia was less successful with her version of *Moses*, by Michelangelo. Perhaps she chose to copy this work because she admired how Moses had led the Jews out of bondage. Edmonia's statue, however, is about one-fourth the size of the original. And, lacking

90

Edmonia Lewis

Edmonia Lewis's copy of Moses *by Michelangelo*

Michelangelo's experience and unique genius, her figure is unevenly proportioned.

Michelangelo, who lived about 400 years before Edmonia was born, was a brilliant painter and an extraordinary sculptor. Before modeling anything, he drew dozens of sketches and drew again directly on the fronts of large blocks of marble. Like the ancient Greeks, he used a hand drill and a claw chisel, and attacked the marble himself before he let an assistant cut away any excess stone. What courage! Edmonia had copied the supreme master! She may not have been capable of copying as well as she would have liked. Still, while working, she must have learned much.

Soon after completing her *Moses* (1875), she began to concentrate on *The Death of Cleopatra*. This statue would become Edmonia's largest work and would later be lost for more than 100 years.

Chapter 8

The Death of Cleopatra

*O*n returning to Rome in 1874, Edmonia found her sculptor companions preparing for America's first Centennial Exposition. This celebration of the nation's first 100 years would be held in 1876 in Philadelphia.

Congress was sending a ship to transport art works from abroad. And Edmonia was invited to send her statues on this ship. Anne Whitney was sending her *Roma*, a withered old woman who symbolized a worn-out Rome; and the popular American sculptor William Wetmore Story sent his statues *Cleopatra* and *Libyan Sybil.*

Wanting to produce a grand original, Edmonia also chose to sculpt a huge statue of Cleopatra for the

Anne Whitney sent her Roma *(left) and William Wetmore Story sent his* Cleopatra *to the Centennial Exhibition in 1876.*

exposition. She knew that she was hardly the first to think about this unusual Egyptian queen. Writers, actors, painters, and other sculptors besides Story had long focused on this dynamic ruler. Now, letting go of the neoclassical style, she challenged herself. What she created became her boldest work.

Edmonia was aware of Cleopatra's unique place in history and wanted to dignify her life. Cleopatra was a Macedonian Greek, not an Egyptian. After Alexander the Great conquered Egypt, the Macedonians ruled the nation for almost 300 years. Cleopatra, a descendant of Ptolemy, was born in 69 B.C.

She came to the throne in Egypt after her father died. By the terms of her father's will and to preserve the kingdom, at the age of 18 she married her younger brother, as was the custom, and they ruled together.

To restore her country's fame, a strong-minded Cleopatra raised an army to fight her brother. Julius Caesar, ruler of the Roman Empire, tried to bring peace between the two. Instead he fell in love with Cleopatra.

Despite Caesar's efforts, Cleopatra declared war. After her brother drowned in a sea battle, she was crowned queen of Egypt and shared the throne with a second brother.

Fearing that Caesar was becoming too powerful, his enemies assassinated him on March 15 in 44 B.C. The respected general Marc Antony replaced Caesar and shared the power with Caesar's grandnephew and adopted son, Octavian. (Edmonia had copied a marble portrait bust of the young Octavian in 1873.)

When Antony and Cleopatra met, they fell in love. Antony gave Cleopatra protection and Roman lands, thereby offending his countrymen. Octavian, angered by Antony's action, prepared for war against them.

After months of fighting, before a battle at sea near Greece, Cleopatra had her luggage brought aboard a ship. As Antony with his men rowed out to meet the enemy (31 B.C.), he watched her set sail for Egypt. Deserting his men, he followed her. The men, feeling abandoned, surrendered to Octavian.

Cleopatra realized that her empire was lost. Rather than live in captivity, she hid her treasures in a tomb that had been built for her in Egypt and made plans to die.

Mistakenly believing that Cleopatra was dead, Antony stabbed himself but survived. A very much alive Cleopatra sent for him. Wounded as he was, he climbed through a high window to reach his love and comfort her before he died.

Octavian and his men invaded Egypt. Knowing she would be paraded through the streets of Rome to be scorned by the people, Cleopatra prepared for death. It is thought that she bathed, dressed, and ate a luxurious meal. Afterward a peasant arrived with a basket of fruit for her. The basket may have contained an asp.

When Octavian found Cleopatra, she had already accepted a bite from the poisonous snake and was lying dead on a royal couch. In a world where most women had no power, this practical queen had ruled several nations during her lifetime.

Edmonia produced an enormous *Cleopatra*, with the pain of death exposed on her face. This sculpture would become the most talked about attraction at the Centennial Exposition.

In Philadelphia, a nervous Edmonia lingered in the center hall. She had seen the committee reject other works. *The New York Times* (December 29, 1876) wrote that she waited for her box to be uncrated. "They [the committee] talked together for a moment, and then I heard the order to place it in such and such position . . . ," she said. The placement concluded, Edmonia went home and had a good cry all by herself.

Edmonia was at the height of her popularity in 1876, and at the Centennial Exposition she won international respect. Her years of study, poverty, persistence, and hard work had paid off. At last her statues—she had also brought along *The Old Arrowmaker*, *Asleep*, and the terra-cotta busts *John Brown*, *Henry Wadsworth Longfellow*, and *Charles Sumner*—were displayed among 673 sculptures, 162 of them by Americans.

The committee awarded 43 certificates of excellence, but none to sculptors. Nonetheless, J.S. Ingram wrote

in *The Centennial Exhibition* that Edmonia's *The Death of Cleopatra* (1876) was "the most remarkable piece of sculpture in the American section."

Over the centuries, Cleopatra had been described as mysterious, desirable, dangerous, ambitious, and fierce. Edmonia's sculpture, however, revealed a complex, intelligent queen—a political achiever. Edmonia had studied medals, 15 portraits on ancient Roman coins, and an antique marble head supposedly of Cleopatra in the Vatican before she modeled her realistic woman in death.

Edmonia showed a Cleopatra who had already accepted the snake bite on her bare breast. Yet, except for the unnatural pose of the head, her Cleopatra appears relaxed. She lies back, her limp left hand hanging loosely over a decorated armrest. Her right hand still clutches the asp. She is shown as a woman who ruled with authority, a woman in control of both her life and her death. The hieroglyphics that decorate the throne are invented symbols.

Edmonia's realistic portrayal of death upset much of the general public. Most people during this time expected statues to be serene and without any sign of suffering or death. They had found the *Cleopatra* by William Wetmore Story more appealing. His

Edmonia Lewis's The Death of Cleopatra, *with its realistic portrayal of death, caused a stir at the Centennial Exhibition.*

neoclassical Grecian woman with her downcast, expressionless face was more acceptable to them. An overabundance of drapery covers the footstools and feet of both Edmonia's and Story's statues. These folds may seem fussy and excessive today. But it is known that Edmonia liked to fold marble swirls of fabric about her figures.

Dramatically placed in the main hall, Edmonia's *Cleopatra* drew thousands of visitors to her side. People either gaped in awe or walked away in disgust. Almost every day Edmonia had a bittersweet experience. Once the father of a former classmate from Oberlin came forward to shake her hand. But the statue embarrassed Philadelphia's African American leaders. Instead of expressing dignity, Edmonia chose to show her subject in a struggle with death.

The Reverend Benjamin T. Tanner, editor of *The Christian Record*, who had encouraged black artists to show their works at the exhibition, tried to ignore Edmonia's contributions. When black painter Robert Douglass, Jr., reviewed the exhibition for Tanner's paper, Edmonia's statues were not even mentioned. Yet, Tanner's son, Henry Ossawa Tanner, was inspired by Edmonia's *Cleopatra*. He would become a painter in Paris and in the early 1900s receive two Legion of Honor medals from the French government for his work.

Edmonia felt that the black community had come more to scoff than to support her. Then there was the stereotyping. One day an art collector and writer, watching Edmonia dust her "Lady," thought that she was a Southern cook or, at best, a housemaid. After they spoke together, he realized he had been talking with an educated, gifted artist.

Before the exhibition closed, reviews began to change. William J. Clark, Jr., wrote in *Great American Sculpture* (1878) of Edmonia's work:

> *Miss Lewis . . . has followed the coins, medals, authentic records, giving Cleopatra an aquiline [beaked] nose and a prominent chin of the Roman type. This Cleopatra . . . more nearly resembles the real heroine of history. . . . This is not a beautiful work, but it is a very original and striking one . . . represented with such skill as to be absolutely repellent. . . . The qualities of the work could only have been produced by a sculptor of genuine endowments."[1]*

The *Oberlin Review* described Edmonia as a "renowned sculptor" and boasted that she had her first art lessons at their college. John Sampson, an educator at Wilberforce University, said after they met that she was "a downright sensible woman . . . of no foolishness, a devoted lover of her race."[2]

Unfortunately, the majority of people ignored the

favorable reviews and continued to think of *Cleopatra* as "absolutely repellent." After the exposition closed, Edmonia stored the statue in a warehouse.

In 1878 it was displayed at Chicago's Interstate Industrial Exposition and later was shown in Chicago's Farwell Hall to raise money for a Catholic charity. Again it drew crowds. Knowing the statue would be too costly to ship back to Italy, Edmonia stored it once more. Then it disappeared.

How and where a 3,015-pound statue, five and a half feet tall, could be moved remains a mystery. Over the next hundred years, writers who referred to *The Death of Cleopatra* suggested that either it was destroyed, possibly for its lovely Carrara marble, or it was lost forever.

That the Egyptian queen was ever found is a miracle. And the twists and turns her journey took over the next 120 years are remarkable.

Somehow in 1892 the statue showed up in a Clark Street saloon in Chicago. No one knows how it happened, but soon afterward "Blind John" Condon, a Chicago gambler, bought *Cleopatra* and moved her to his Harlem Race Track in Forest Park, on the outskirts of Chicago. There he had it placed on the gravesite of his beloved racehorse, also named Cleopatra.

In the 1920s the racetrack was remade into a golf course, but *Cleopatra* stayed where she was. In 1942, during World War II, the Navy built a torpedo factory on the property. Again, because Condon had added a clause to his deed preventing any disturbance to his horse's grave, "*Cleopatra* stood right where Mr. Condon wanted it," someone said.

Around 1971 the United States Postal Service inherited the property. Before the construction of Chicago's Bulk Mail Center, *Cleopatra* was carried off to a Cicero salvage yard. There she stood among debris in all kinds of weather. One day in 1985 fire chief Harold Adams, on a routine inspection of the yard, rediscovered the queen.

"I'm just a layman," he told a reporter, "but the minute I saw her, I knew that statue was something beautiful. She was like a big white ghost out there between all the heavy machinery, and [she was] crying out to be saved."[3]

With help from his son's Boy Scout troop, he moved the statue to a safer place. Amateurs though they were, the scouts, with good intentions, cleaned and painted over the graffiti and stains with a creamy white latex paint to cover the tunic. They also painted the flesh pink and made several improper repairs.

Adams sought expert help but did not find it. Occasionally a local paper publicized his cause. Finally in 1988 the Forest Park Historical Society "adopted" *Cleopatra* and brought her to a nearby shopping mall. When the mall changed owners, the Society placed *Cleopatra* in storage.

The statue was in bad shape. The roses and leaves on Cleopatra's robe and also her hands were worn down. Pieces were missing. The chin, nose, sandals, and snake were broken. Dr. Frank Orland, the society's director, began to inquire into the identity of Edmonia Lewis, whose signature was on the side of the statue. He planned to make ill-advised, unprofessional changes of his own. Even after years of neglect and vandalism, Sotheby's, the international auction house, valued *Cleopatra* "as is" at close to $150,000.

Fortunately, a staff member of the Metropolitan Museum of Art in New York recalled an inquiry that Marilyn Richardson, a professor at the Massachusetts Institute of Technology, had placed in a *New York Times Book Review*. She had been collecting information and searching for *Cleopatra* for years.

A contact was made. On arrival in Forest Park, Marilyn Richardson, after one glance, knew that her search was over! Rising out of stored Christmas decorations and paper Thanksgiving turkeys, there *Cleopatra* stood, a priceless piece of African American-Chippewa history!

In 1994 the Forest Park Historical Society donated the statue to the Smithsonian Institution's National Museum of American Art (NMAA). Expert conservator Andrzej Dajnowski began the repair work.

George Gurney, sculpture curator at the museum, had unexpectedly discovered an 1895 photograph of the original *Cleopatra*. Using it as the "blueprint," the restorers stripped most of the two surfaces of paint and the graffiti and stains beneath the paint. Some paint spread by the Boy Scouts was left, to avoid removing more of the delicate marble. The missing areas were filled in with a mixture of new, crushed marble and acrylic resin. Gurney said, "We left signs of wear and tear as part of this statue's extraordinary history." Restorers replaced the hands, feet, nose, snake, and headdress; the total cost of the restoration was $30,000.

On June 7, 1996, *The Death of Cleopatra* was officially welcomed into its new home—the National

Museum of American Art in Washington, D.C. Three days later rave reviews began to arrive. Jo Ann Lewis of the *Washington Post* wrote on June 10, 1996: "Though dealing with a woman from the distant past, a queen in neoclassical guise, Lewis . . . amplified Cleopatra's humanity."

The Daily Record of Morris County, New Jersey, said on June 16, 1996: "The reconditioned *Cleopatra* again exudes the sparkle of its original beauty."

On July 14, 1996, the *Chicago Tribune* headlined its story: "SAVING GRACE, *Cleopatra* rescues sculptor from art history's scrapheap." Michael Killian, staff writer, said that the Smithsonian museum had "unveiled a thing of surpassing beauty . . . a sweet, proud, sad Cleopatra."

The Tribune, Antiques Magazine, and *The Arts Weekly* (July 19, 1996) called Edmonia "a serious, accomplished artist," and *Antiques* referred to *Cleopatra* as a "long missing masterwork."

Long after the 1876 Centennial Exposition, and years before *Cleopatra* was rediscovered, a four-year-old appreciated the queen for other reasons. Lynn C. Flood, of Virginia, in a letter (July 1, 1996) to George Gurney wrote:

This statue sat in my back yard when I lived in Forest Park, Ill. I lived in naval officers quarters. My father worked at the Great Lakes Naval Base. The houses were built in a circle around a central green. This statue sat in the middle of the green. My family lived there in the early 50's (1953–1955?).

Cleopatra holds a very sentimental place in my brothers' and my hearts. She was the center of our universe. Whenever we were to meet our friends, it was at the statue. (We were too young to know her as Cleopatra.) There were many games of king of the statue, and . . . she was the free base for playing tag. One of the best days of my childhood was the day I was able to climb her without a boost from my big brother. In fact all of the kids in the neighborhood claimed her as their property.

This may give you a lead to where Cleopatra has been.

Curator Gurney believes the artist and her statue have "a certain undeniable majesty in life and in death. . . . Each chose not to submit to the will of her conquerors and [each] controlled her own life. [Edmonia] Lewis made her mark against incredible odds."

The world today is richer because Edmonia, listening to her own voice, did not give up.

Chapter
9

Edmonia's Legacy—
How Good Was She?

After Edmonia gave the world a vital *Cleopatra*, her life changed once again. In the late 1880s the public's interest in neoclassical art began to wane, and bronze sculptures became more popular than marble. Still, she worked steadily.

The Philadelphia League ordered a bust of John Brown. The city of New York commissioned a bust of Lincoln, and a friend of Harriet Hosmer bought a copy of *The Old Arrowmaker*. But mostly Edmonia concentrated on altarpieces, religious statues, and wall reliefs. Her patrons were English, Italian, and Catholic friends.

In 1877 the former president Ulysses S. Grant asked her to do his portrait. Edmonia first observed him on the streets of Rome. Then she invited him to pose for her final corrections. Like Longfellow, Grant was pleased with the results.

Her last known major commission was *The Adoration of the Magi* (1883). This grouping included the baby Jesus and three wisemen—an Asian, a Caucasian, and an African. It was made for the original Church of St. Francis in Baltimore and presently is listed as lost.

In 1885 Edmonia and 29 other artists signed a petition to Congress written by William Story. This proposal, which was approved, asked for the removal of taxes on artwork being brought into the United States. Quite possibly the repeal of this law enabled American museums to build up the vast collections of prints, paintings, and sculptures they own today.

Little is known about Edmonia's later years. Frederick Douglass wrote that he had met her on a walk in Rome in 1887. They had known each other in Boston. After a visit to her studio with his second wife, Helen Louise, he wrote in his diary:

> We came into a pleasant room with a commanding view. [Edmonia] lives here, and here she plies her fingers in her art as a sculptress . . . cheerful, happy, and successful. She offered to serve us in any way she could. . . . Constantly speaking Italian has somewhat impaired her English.[1]

Edmonia's Legacy—How Good Was She?

Her knowledge of Italian may have actually been helpful to the Douglasses, because Edmonia traveled with them as their guide to Naples and Pompeii.

Where and when Edmonia died remains one more unsolved mystery. Records show that she signed the guest book in the United States Embassy in Rome in 1909. *The Rosary*, an American Catholic magazine, reported in February 1909 that though "advanced in years, she is still with us." She was seen in Rome in 1911, and historians believe she died that year. However, this date has not been confirmed.

A recent rumor suggests that Edmonia may have died in Marin County, California, and that she may have been buried in an unmarked grave in San Francisco. The California state records of death certificates (1905–1920) do not, however, list her name. Edmonia vanished and her works were forgotten—until women and African Americans sought their own histories in the 1960s.

Since the unexpected rediscovery of *The Death of Cleopatra*, news reporters have questioned why most people have never heard about her and have asked how good a sculptor she was. A look at the past may help us understand why Edmonia Lewis was forgotten.

Before and during Edmonia's lifetime, white males controlled the art world. They excluded African American and women artists from exhibits in museums and galleries. They forbade or restricted enrollment into most art schools. Institutions rarely purchased art by women and African Americans. Patrons were scarce, and only on occasion could these artists display their works in a local store window, a private home, or a church. In the nineteenth century, American museums would have been closed to works by black artist Henry Ossawa Tanner and Edmonia Lewis. Most of Edmonia's pieces were bought by African Americans and abolitionists.

Yet by no means was Edmonia alone in the difficulties she faced as a nonwhite artist. African Americans who chose to become artists had to over-come immense obstacles. They either found patrons who encouraged them, studied with reputable white artists, or taught themselves.

In the 1700s Joshua Johnston, a free black man, became a self-taught, traveling portrait painter. In 1835, as a teenager, Patrick Reason apprenticed him-self to an engraver and later became an independent engraver. In 1836, Robert S. Duncanson established himself as a "professional artist" in New Orleans.

Edmonia's Legacy—How Good Was She?

Seventeen years later the Anti-Slavery League sponsored his trip to study in Italy.

At the grand Centennial Exposition of 1876, Edward Bannister, the painter who helped Edmonia sell replicas of her Robert Gould Shaw bust in Boston, won a bronze medal for his painting *Under the Oaks*. When he tried to claim the award, he was refused entry to the exhibition hall through the front door because of his color. He received his prize only after identifying himself.

In 1879 the Pennsylvania Academy of Fine Arts accepted Henry Ossawa Tanner into a class of males, aged 20 to 60. He was the only black.

One classmate, Joseph Pennell, later described a racist act that Tanner remembered the rest of his life. "One night his [Tanner] easel was carried out into the middle of Broad Street . . . he was firmly tied to it and left there."[2]

After Tanner settled in Paris, at the age of 32 he submitted several paintings to the powerful Paris Salon exhibition. This event annually attracted thousands of Parisians.

Tanner received an honorable mention in 1896 for his now famous *Daniel in the Lion's Den*, and the following year the Musée de Luxembourg purchased his *Resurrection of Lazarus.* Although his work received many honors and prizes, Tanner gained only minor fame. And, because of the racial prejudice he experienced in his native country, he never again lived in the United States. While Tanner, like Edmonia, was proud of his African heritage, he refused to paint only those subjects that reflected his blackness.

Throughout the ages, society has dealt perhaps even more harshly with women artists. For centuries women had posed for and were the subjects of paintings and sculptures by male artists. If women painted, they supposedly did so for amusement. Yet hundreds of women—mothers, daughters, sisters, and wives—painted at home. In the 1600s a few became artists in the rich courts of Spain, Portugal, and France. Others worked for a male relative or studied privately with a male teacher. French art schools opened classes to women on a quota basis in 1790. Sometimes, when they were kept out of life-drawing classes, the women posed for one another. A glimpse at a handful of now-famous women artists (all white) indicates how some of them survived.

Louise Moillon (1610–1696) became one of France's best painters of still lifes. At a young age she made a deal with her stepfather to share her earnings.

Edmonia's Legacy—How Good Was She?

More than 200 years later, one of her paintings sold for $120,000. Elizabeth Vigée-Lebrun (1755–1842), who taught other women to paint, is remembered as a fine portrait painter. Today a self-portrait with her child hangs in the Louvre in Paris. Rosa Bonheur (1822–1899), also French, filled huge canvases with proud horses and other animals. Bonheur gave up sculpting to avoid competing with her brother, Isadore. Her works, too, hang in the Louvre.

The American Jane Stuart (1812–1888) came to painting through her father, Gilbert Stuart, who painted America's favorite portrait of President George Washington. She ground her father's colors and filled in backgrounds of his portraits until he died. Then, in her own studio, she supported her family by selling copies of his works.

French artist Berthe Morisot (1841–1895) joined a group of young painters who, in rebellion against standards set by the Paris Salon judges, painted with bright pure colors. Calling themselves "Impressionists," they filled canvases with street scenes, landscapes, and people enjoying simple pleasures amid nature and outdoor light.

American-born Mary Cassatt (1845–1921), painter of mothers and children, moved to Paris and became a close friend of artist Edgar Degas. She convinced wealthy American visitors to buy the work of many impressionists.

When the Impressionists exhibited together in 1875—a year before Edmonia's remarkable *Cleopatra* was criticized in Philadelphia—Parisians ridiculed these new paintings unmercifully. Albert Wolff of *Le Figaro* wrote: "Five or six lunatics . . . among them a woman [Berthe Morisot]—have met to exhibit their work."[3] Today paintings by Degas, Renoir, Monet, Pissarro, Cezanne, Cassatt, and Morisot are exhibited in museums around the world.

The American women sculptors who chose to create in Rome, except for Edmonia, came from educated, prosperous families. Author Henry James described them as "a strange sisterhood of . . . 'lady sculptors' who settled upon the seven hills in a white marmorean flock."[4] *Marmorean* referred to their preference for marble.

He criticized their attitudes and their masculine clothing. He referred to Edmonia as a "negress" and suggested that her color ought not be the reason for her gaining fame. Edmonia would have agreed heartily. She had devoted her life to becoming an accepted artist. She believed in the United States Constitution and wanted to see the words in the Pledge of Allegiance—*liberty and justice for all*—include her people.

Among the women sculptors, the American Harriet Hosmer (1830–1908) was considered the most professional. Reared by her physician father after her mother's death, she studied sculpting at the University of St. Louis. Then she learned anatomy in a medical school, which was almost unheard of for a woman at that time.

Edmonia must have heard about Harriet Hosmer's stately *Zenobia* and how badly it was received when she brought it to the United States in 1864. Picky critics pointed out many supposed flaws, saying the statue's weight was imbalanced and the figure "lacked fullness at the lips . . . and had a cramped little toe on its left foot."[5] Still, it sold to a rich New Yorker for $2,500 above the freight costs.

In Rome, too, rumors persisted that Hosmer's stonecutter or her teacher, John Gibson, had transferred her clay models into marble. Ignoring all gossip, Hosmer said, "I honor those [women] who step broadly forward and in spite of ridicule and criticism, pave the way for women of the next generation."[6]

Anne Whitney, too, had felt the sting of discrimination. After she moved from Rome back to

Harriet Hosmer stands beside her imposing statue of Thomas Hart Benton.

Edmonia's Legacy—How Good Was She?

Massachusetts, in 1871 she entered a competition to create a memorial to honor Charles Sumner. Numbers replaced sculptors' names to ensure fairness. The judges chose Anne Whitney's model. But after learning that the winner was a woman, the committee gave the commission to a male artist. Finally, in 1902, Harvard University officials placed the Whitney bronze statue of the Senator in front of their old law school.

In light of this history of discrimination, it is remarkable that Edmonia Lewis was able to achieve all that she did.

People viewing Edmonia's sculptures may question why she created Native American and African American figures in white marble. Neoclassical artists of her time were producing Greco-Roman statues in marble, and most marble was white. Yet, what if Edmonia had chiseled *The Old Arrowmaker* in red marble, would the color have heightened the negative image of "redskin" that already existed?

Edmonia had a strong sense of her true talent. Throughout her life she ignored racial barriers and negative advice. Against daunting odds she mastered sculptural skills and produced more than 60 works. Too many are still missing today.

Edmonia Lewis

With faith in herself and her ideals, Edmonia honored in her work former slaves and the cause of freedom. She loved the innocence of children and the nation's courageous men and women (real and legendary) who pushed forward to obtain human rights for everyone. Her statues also expressed her deep gratitude for the gift of life.

Beneath the surface view of her quietly posed figures and thoughtful faces, the fiery voice of Wildfire may have also been calling out. Edmonia may have wanted to tell us: "Look at what *I* created. With support, imagine what my people could do. Let's unite to bring forth the beauty and talent in all people. Set my people free!"

A woman ahead of her time, Edmonia was a trail-blazer. She was the first Chippewa–African American woman sculptor and the first African American artist who received international fame and supported herself through her art.

With the miraculous rediscovery of *The Death of Cleopatra*, there is a growing interest in this tiny woman who has given the world such highly original sculptures. Edmonia Lewis richly deserves the praise she has begun to receive.

Sculptures by Edmonia Lewis referred to in
Edmonia Lewis: Wildfire In Marble

Date	Title
1864–1865	John Brown medallions
1865	Robert Gould Shaw (plaster replicas)
1866	Anne Quincy Waterston
	A Freed Woman and Her Child
	The Old Arrowmaker and His Daughter
	(carved 1872, at least 3 versions)
1866–1867	The Marriage of Hiawatha
1867–1868	Forever Free
1867–1868	Robert Gould Shaw (marble)
1868	Hagar in the Wilderness
	(a second statue 1875)
1869	Madonna Holding the Christ Child
1869–1871	Hiawatha
	Minnehaha
	Henry Wadsworth Longfellow
1870	Abraham Lincoln
1871	Asleep
1872	Awake
1873	Poor Cupid
	Young Octavian
	Moses
1874	Hygieia
1876	The Death of Cleopatra
1877–1878	General Ulysses S. Grant
1878–1879	John Brown
1883	The Adoration of the Magi

Chapter Notes

Introduction

1. Philip Montsano, "The Mystery of the San Jose Statues," *Urban West*, March-April 1968, 25–27.
2. Ibid., 25–27.
3. Langston Hughes, Milton Meltzer, and others, *A Pictorial History of Africans in America* (New York: Crown Publishers, 1995), 93–94.
4. Ibid., 93–94.

Chapter 1

1. Romare Bearden and Harry Henderson, *A History of African American Artists 1792 to the Present* (New York: Pantheon Books, 1993), 55.
2. Sylvia G.L. Dannett, *Profiles of Negro Womenhood 1619-1900 Vol. 1* (Yonkers, NY: Educational Heritage, 1964), 119.
3. Bearden, 56.
4. Dannett, 119.

Chapter 2

1. *Friends of Oberlin* flyer, 1996.
2. Geoffrey H. Blodgett, "John Mercer Langston and the Case of Edmonia Lewis: Oberlin, 1862," *Journal of Negro History* (53 No. 3), 202.
3. Bearden, 56.

Chapter 3

1. Blodgett, 205.

People

2. Ibid., 209.

3. L. Maria Child, article in _Broken Fetter_, March 3, 1865, Oberlin College Archives.

Chapter 4

1. Bearden, 60.

2. Dannett, 120.

3. Child.

4. Ibid.

5. Ibid.

6. Dannett, 121–122.

7. Ibid., 121–122.

8. Lynda R. Hartigan, _Sharing Traditions: Five Black Artists in Nineteenth-Century America_ (Washington, DC: National Museum of American Art, 1985), 89.

9. Dannett, 121-122.

10. Bearden, 60.

Chapter 5

1. Bearden, 66.

2. Dolly Sherwood, _Harriet Hosmer, American Sculptor_ (Columbia, MO: University of Missouri Press, 1991), 259.

3. James Porter, _Modern Negro Art_ (Washington, DC: Howard University Press, 1992), 171-172.

4. Ibid., 171–172.

5. Ibid., 171–172.

Chapter 6

1. Hartigan, 94.
2. Edward Wagenknecht, *Longfellow: A Full Length Portrait* (New York: Longman's Green & Co., 1955), 205.
3. Ibid., 75.

Chapter 7

1. Samuel Lewis's Obituary in *Avant Courier* (Bozeman, MT), April 6, 1896.

Chapter 8

1. William J. Clark, *Great American Sculptures* (Philadelphia: Barrel, 1878), 1441–1442.
2. Bearden, 75.
3. Ron Grossman, "Saviors Vie for Cleopatra," *Chicago Tribune*, June 20, 1988.

Chapter 9

1. Bearden, 76.
2. Dewey Mosby and others, *Henry Ossawa Tanner* (Philadelphia: Museum of Art, 1990), 59.
3. John Rewald, *History of Impressionism* (New York: Museum of Modern Art, 1973), 378.
4. Henry James, *William Wetmore Story and His Friends* (Jersey City, NJ: Da Capo, 1969), 75.
5. Sherwood, 181.
6. Charlotte Streifer Rubenstein, *American Women Sculptors* (Boston: G.K. Hall & Co., 1990), 44-45.

Selected Bibliography

Articles

Bearden, Romare. "More on Edmonia Lewis." *Art in America* (November–December 1974), p. 168.

"Biography of a Bozeman Barber." Bozeman, MT, *Avant Courier*, April 6, 1896.

Blodgett, H. Geoffrey. "John Mercer Langston and the Case of Edmonia Lewis: Oberlin, 1862." *Journal of Negro History*, 53 (July 1968), pp. 201–218.

Burgard, Timothy Anglin. "Edmonia Lewis and Henry Wadsworth Longfellow—Images and Identities." *American Art Review*, 7 No. 1 (February–March 1995), pp. 114–117.

Child, L. Maria. *Broken Fetter* (March 3, 1865). Oberlin College Archives.

May Stephen. "The Object at Hand." *Smithsonian* (September 1996), pp. 16–20.

Montesano, Philip. "The Mystery of the San Jose Statues." *Urban West* (March–April 1968), pp. 88–90.

Richardson, Marilyn. "Edmonia Lewis." *Harvard Magazine* (April 1986).

———. "Edmonia Lewis' *The Death of Cleopatra:* Myth and Identity." *International Review of African American Art,* 12 No. 2 (April–June 1995), pp. 36–52.

Tufts, Eleanor. "Edmonia Lewis, Afro-Indian Neo-classicist." *Art in America*, 62 (July–August 1974), pp. 71–72.

Books

Bearden, Romare, and Harry Henderson. *A History of African American Artists From 1792 to the Present.* New York: Pantheon Books, 1993.

Dannett, Sylvia G.L. *Profiles of Negro Womanhood 1619-1900*, Vol. 1. Yonkers, NY: Educational Heritage, 1964.

Fine, Elsa Honig. "Edmonia Lewis." *Women & Art: A History of Women Painters from the Renaissance to the 20th Century.* Montclair, NJ: Allanheld & Schram, 1978.

Greene, Jaqueline D. *The Chippewa.* New York: Franklin Watts, 1993.

Hartigan, Lynda R. *Sharing Traditions: Five Black Artists in Nineteenth-Century America.* Washington, DC: National Museum of American Art, 1985.

Hughes, Langston, Milton Meltzer, and others. *A Pictorial History of Africans in America*, 6th ed. New York: Crown Publishers, 1995.

James, Edward T., and Jane W. James. *Notable American Women 1607–1950: A Biographical Dictionary.* Cambridge, MA: Harvard University Press, 1971.

James, Henry. *William Wetmore Story and His Friends.* Jersey City, NJ: Da Capo, 1969.

Mathews, Marcia M. *Henry Ossawa Tanner: American Artist.* Chicago: University of Chicago Press, 1995.

Mosby, Dewey, and others. *Henry Ossawa Tanner.* Philadelphia: Museum of Art, 1990.

Porter, James. *Modern Negro Art.* Washington, DC: Howard University Press, 1992.

Rewald, John. *History of Impressionism.* New York: Museum of Modern Art, 1973.

Rubenstein, Charlotte Streifer. *American Women Sculptors.* Boston: C. K. Hall, Co., 1990.

Sherwood, Dolly. *Harriet Hosmer: American Sculptor.* Columbia, MO: University of Missouri Press, 1991.

Stanley, Diane, and Peter Vennema. *Cleopatra.* New York: Morrow, 1994.

Wagenknecht, Edward. *Longfellow: A Full Length Portrait.* New York: Longmans Green, 1955.

Wittkower, Rudolf. *Sculpture: Processes & Principles.* New York: Harper & Row, 1977.

*I*ndex